History of Technology

History of Technology

Seventh Annual Volume, 1982

Edited by

A. RUPERT HALL and NORMAN SMITH

Imperial College, London

MANSELL PUBLISHING LIMITED

ISBN 0 7201 1663 5

ISSN 0307-5451

Mansell Publishing Limited,
6 All Saints Street, London N1 9RL

First published 1982

©Mansell Publishing Limited and the Contributors

Distributed in the United States and Canada by The H. W. Wilson Company,
950 University Avenue, Bronx, New York 10452

British Library Cataloguing in Publication Data

History of technology.—7th annual volume (1982)
   1. Technology—History—Periodicals
   609   T15
   ISBN 0-7201-1663-5

Printed and bound in Great Britain by
Butler & Tanner Ltd, Frome and London

Contents

Preface

This year our seven papers, as well as presenting topics from a variety of periods, illustrate some of the different ways in which the evidence of historical technology must be approached and handled. The piece by Dr Foley and his colleagues on ancient gearing, for instance, makes use, in part, of experiments on replicas, a technique with more potential for unravelling the obscurities of machines and processes than is perhaps generally realized or rationally exploited. Professor Malinowski's contribution on ancient cements displays facets of the problems of dealing with archaeological evidence and reconciling it with contemporary writings. Professor Boyer's depends on impressively thorough investigation of masses of medieval documents while Michael Fores has critically reviewed a single source. Francis Evans' essay is a valuable and timely reappraisal of a traditional material's survival and development through an epoch commonly assumed to have been dominated by metals and plastics. Occasionally we like to 'quote' historic documents and Professor Tucker's contribution is especially interesting for being an English engineer's view of the nature and purpose of industrial research. And finally, but by no means least, it is a pleasure to include an article by a former student of ours, David Compton, on the complex interplay between theory and practice, supply and demand, in the establishment of the internal combustion engine as a practical and influential prime mover.

The history of technology is truly a multi-faceted discipline whose continuing development will require may types of problem to be tackled by a great variety of techniques.

A. RUPERT HALL
NORMAN A. F. SMITH

Water Mills: a Problem for the Bridges and Boats of Medieval France*

MARJORIE NICE BOYER

In the Middle Ages bridges attracted buildings — towers, chapels, dwellings, shops and workshops, toll houses, even hospitals, and especially mills. In population centres, like Paris or Toulouse, the roadways of bridges were lined with shops and houses so that the passerby might think himself on an extension of the street. At small towns, buildings on the bridge were rare, but in both cases mills were common, whether attached to the structure or adjacent to it. Yet complaints about mills were frequent. They interfered with navigation and aggravated the effects of floods, and their operation damaged the bridge itself. It is the purpose of the present article to examine the exact relationship of mills and bridges and the reasons for the unhappiness of boatmen and bridge owners with the siting of mills on, at, or next to a bridge.

Mills and Bridges

The intimate association between bridges and water mills lasted more than a thousand years — from the early Middle Ages into the nineteenth century — and was to be found in Switzerland, Spain, England, France and Italy. Our earliest evidence for floating mills, those of Belisarius during the siege of Rome in 537, notes that they were fastened 'where the flow of water comes down from the arch of the bridge with greatest force'.[1] The combination of bridges and mills was attested at Geneva in the year 563 when 'a bridge with mills' was noted in a chronicle.[2] At Paris in the ninth century the gift by Charles the Bald of the Grand Pont to the bishop of that city included the bridge, the water of the area, the mills and 'whatever else seemed to belong to the bridge'.[3] The phrase is an appropriate one. Mills did indeed belong to medieval bridges. Between the years 1000 and 1500 there were mills in connection with bridges at Albi, Angers, Autun, Auxerre, Beaugency, Blois, Cheny (Yonne), Chinon, Compiègne, La Ferté-Milon (Aisne), Laval, Lyons on the Saône, Mayenne, Millau, Poitiers, Pont-de-

*In preparing this paper, I have received assistance and suggestions from many quarters. I wish to thank Norman Smith, Bert S. Hall, Timothy H. Boyer, Brooke Hindle, Marie-Thérèse d'Alverny, Louis C. Hunter, Kenneth D. Boyer and Suzanne P. Tainter.

l'Arche, Pontoise, Ponts-de-Cé, Pont-sur-Yonne, Provins, Sens, Troyes, Villeneuve-sur-Yonne, and many other localities.

The synthesis of mills and bridges was partially based on a community of interests. Both millers and bridge builders located their structures to serve the community, the larger the better. Both groups were much concerned with the geography of the site. A wide stream with a swift current meant more pressure to bridge it and a greater probability that millers would take advantage of a fine source of power and construct a mill. A sound bottom and banks such as to afford easy access were important to bridge builders and millers, while the latter joined boatmen in a concern for an adequate flow of water. There were definite advantages to a mill owner in siting his mills near a bridge. Such a location allowed the mill to draw customers from both sides of the stream, and there were certain logistical and technological bonuses available to the owner of a mill at a bridge. The advantages of the relationship between mills and bridges, however, were not reciprocal. Mills were at best an inconvenience to bridge owners and at worst a cause of the deterioration of the structure. Both millers and bridge owners appear to have considered boatmen more in the light of an unavoidable nuisance than anything else. This sentiment seems to have been heartily reciprocated by boatmen.

In a consideration of the attraction of bridges for mills a distinction should be made between the *moulin-du-pont*, literally 'mill of the bridge' but more appropriately translated as 'mill at the bridge', and a *pont-du-moulin*, literally 'bridge of the mill' but more realistically translated 'bridge to a mill'. In the former case there were mills in connection with a bridge constructed to afford passage across the stream; in the second, the bridge was built to give access to a mill located in the water, away from the banks. By far the most famous *pont-du-moulin* was the Pont-aux-Meuniers at Paris. It was built after the destruction of the Grand Pont by a great flood, one which washed out the Petit Pont also, on 21 December 1296. The old Grand Pont was replaced by a new and timber version, passable by 12 November 1297, but the wooden bridge was slightly upstream from the old stone one. The proprietors of mills below the old Grand Pont found themselves owning sites in the Seine at some distance from the new bridge. Each owner rebuilt his mill and the part of the bridge necessary to reach it. In the early fourteenth century there were ten mills in eleven arches and the last one was adjacent to the great arch kept open for navigation. Here at first the bridge ended without crossing to the other bank, but it was subsequently completed across the Seine.[4]

Despite the fame of the millers' bridge (Pont-aux-Meuniers) there was nothing unusual about it except that it was built and maintained by a series of mill owners rather than by one. At Paris mills usually had their own walkway or bridge connecting them with the river bank. Charters of Sainte-Magloire show that in 1296 the Templars possessed a walkway to reach their two mills in the Seine and that in 1317 the bishop of Paris was allowed to construct a footbridge 8 feet wide to his mills at the Planches de Mibray.[5] The prior and brothers of the hospital of Saint John of Jerusalem had a 'certain pont ou alée' to go on foot or on horseback to a mill which they had at the end of the Grand Pont towards the palace.[6] The provost of the *marchands de l'eau*, the Hanse of Paris, kept a jealous eye on all obstructions to navigation on the Seine. When in 1203 the brothers of the Temple wished to link their mills to the port de Grève, the provost of the merchants insisted that the arches of the walkway should be at least three toises (5.84 m) wide to allow the merchants' boats to pass up and down the Seine under them.[7]

Some of the *moulins-du-pont* are described as next to or near a bridge. There was one *juxta pontem* at Compiègne in 1183 and a *molendinum prope pontem* of Saint-Julien (Marne), commune of Pierre, in 1239.[8] In such a case, calling the mill a mill-of-the-bridge may have been only a means of distinguishing it from its fellows in the region. On the other hand, in some cases the obstruction constituted by the bridge meant a significantly larger volume of water upstream, a point of great interest to millers. There were many mills above bridges. For example, at Albi in the thirteenth century there were three mills upstream from the bridge and very many at Paris were similarly situated.[9]

There could be important advantages for mill owners (although not for bridges or boatmen) in locating a mill 'in', 'on', or 'below' a bridge, and the utility could extend beyond a location at a centre of town activities — the bridge. Easy access could be had to mills directly from the roadway in cases where the mill house rested on supports fixed in the masonry of the bridge or was built directly against its downstream side. The mill could be reached from the roadway of the old bridges of Blois, Vernon, Millau, Ponts-de-Cé and Pont-de-l'Arche.[10] The mills at Corbeil (Fig. 1) illustrate this type of access and the picture should be compared with the remains of the old mills at Moret-sur-Loing. There the downstream mill house is right on the roadway and the upstream mills can be reached from the bridge by first descending a staircase outside the downstream mill and then passing under the bridge.[11] Some *moulins-du-pont* providing direct access from the bridge had walls touching those of the bridge. Such were the *moulins-du-pont* at Tours, at Saumur and at the Pont-de-Treilles at Angers.[12] At Albi the mill in the arch next to the drawbridge could be reached either from the bridge or by water at the base of the pier, where the mill had a port.[13]

Access directly from the roadway of a bridge to a mill seems to have been uncommon, but a favourite location for a mill was in one of the arches below, that is, downstream from, a bridge, in some cases at least because of a more rapid flow of water below it. In 1203 the lord of Beaugency granted to the convent of Notre-Dame of that place 'unum stallum in archa pontis'.[14] King Philip I in 1070 gave to the convent of Saint-Martin-des-Champs, for the benefit of the poor and pilgrims, a mill described as 'in Magno Ponte'.[15] This phrase has been translated as 'sur le Grand Pont', but the mill was actually located downstream from an arch of the bridge.[16] A stronger current for efficient operation of the mill below the bridge and easier access, whether from the roadway of the bridge or the possibility of drawing customers from both sides of the stream, were among the factors accounting for the clustering of mills at bridges.

Figure 1. Mills at Corbeil in the time of Louise XI. Paris, Archives Nationales, S2116.

TECHNOLOGY AND TYPES OF MILLS

The relationship among mills, boats and bridges was much affected by the technology and types of mills. There were stationary and floating mills, but in each case the mill wheel seems to have been vertical and undershot.[17] An undershot wheel is operable in a strong current even without a mill race, but an overshot wheel, to take advantage of the fact that it uses relatively little water, requires a chute to direct it to a point high up on the wheel. To divert the stream and to raise the sluice to the required height would have been more expensive than the rows of piling which sufficed for many mill races and would probably have touched off one of those bitter quarrels over water rights so typical of the fourteenth and fifteenth centuries. For example, in 1324 Robert Miete, bourgeois of Paris, was condemned to demolish his water gate and sluice as they deflected the waters of the Seine from the Pont-aux-Meuniers, to the distress of the millers there.[18]

Vertical wheels are indicated in two lists of parts bought to repair mills, one belonging to the abbey of Saint Magloire at Paris and dating from 1299 and the other the property of the château of Vaucluse and dating from 1414.[19] Both note the horizontal axle and gears necessary to transfer the movement of a vertical wheel to the mill stones in the mill house. The Vaucluse document mentions the water wheel with its axle and at the end of the axle the small wheel (*rouet*) whose teeth engaged the lantern wheel (*lanterne*) at the end of the iron bar passing through the lower mill stone to make the upper one revolve. The gearing may be seen in the illumination from the *Life of Saint Denis*, dated 1317 (Fig. 2). The same picture shows the hopper for pouring grain, the casing surrounding the mill stones and the funnel to deliver the flour into a tub. Both the *Life of Saint Denis* and the fifteenth-century drawing of mills at Corbeil show vertical wheels (Fig. 1). The drawing of the mills at Corbeil shows the water gates and mill wheels which appear to have radial floatboards. The wheels have been raised above water level and the left end of the axle is shown fixed in a slot high enough to accommodate lifting the wheel, a procedure which Bélidor in his *Architecture hydraulique* (1737–53) mentions as essential to allow the wheel to be lowered in times of drought and raised to avoid flood damage.[20]

Technological reasons contributed to the large numbers of mills at the same place in medieval France. At Paris, in addition to the ten mills at the Pont-aux-Meuniers between the right bank and the great arch left open for navigation, there were at least fifty-five in the waters of the Seine between the tip of the Ile-Notre-Dame or Saint-Louis and the Pont-aux-Meuniers. The large number of mills at the same site was not merely a question of rivalry between owners, for frequently one owner possessed several mills. For example, at the Pont-sur-Yonne in 1213–14 the Dean and Chapter received permission to put a mill in each of the two arches of the bridge; and in the eleventh century the abbey of Jumièges was allowed to install three mills and fishponds in between the piers of the Pont-de-l'Arche.[21] Brooke Hindle has suggested to me as the explanation for the proliferation at the same location of water mills belonging to a single owner the impracticability

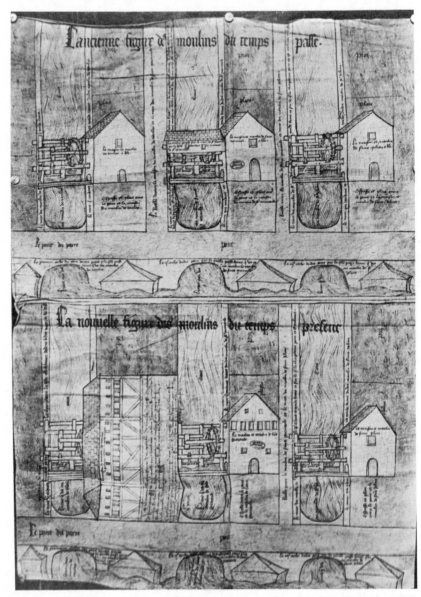

Figure 2. Mills downstream from a bridge at Paris about 1317. Paris. B. N., MS fr. 2092, fol. 37v.

of increasing the size of the mill stones; to meet the demand for greater output it was therefore necessary to increase the number of mills.[22] This technological limitation meant such a large number of mills that at some places they tended to block the stream, making difficulties for navigation and increasing damage from floods.

Medieval mills in France were either stationary or floating, *moulins terriers* or *moulins à bateau*. The grinding mechanism in both types seems to have been about the same. Nothing seems to be known about the exact arrangements of boat mills in medieval France, but Forbes has published a woodcut of the harbour of Cologne in 1499 with a floating mill consisting of a water wheel and the two boats between which it is suspended.[23] By the seventeenth century there were two types of floating mills in France, one the two-boat type and the other consisting of a single boat with a water wheel on either side. In the modern period at Avignon the bigger boat with the mill house was 18 to 20 m long and the smaller boat, which supported one end of the axle of the water wheel, was 10 to 12 m long and 2 to 2.3 m wide.[24] In the seventeenth century at Avignon and at Lyons the two-boat type was preferred and on the Seine in the modern period both types were in use.[25] In the eighteenth century there was much interest in various types of mills. Experiments made in 1775 proved that the single-boat type was the less efficient of the two kinds of floating mills. The two water wheels, on either side of the boat's prow, which divided the stream, received much less power from the river than a water wheel in a guide channel, as was the case in the two-boat type, which could also have a water gate. In addition, the two boats provided greater stability than the single one.[26] Floating mills made their adjustment to their environment in the shape of developing water wheels different from those of land-based mills. They had fewer and longer paddle boards, 5 to 6m long as compared with the 60 to 70 cm of stationary mills. (The reader may recall the paddle wheels of the Mississippi steam boats.)

Advantages of boat mills included cheaper construction (a mill race was unnecessary), the condition of the river bottom for pile-driving was irrelevant, and at some places it was possible, by the use of floating mills, to augment the capacity for producing flour without injuring property rights. For example, the monks of Marmoutier in 1138 were given permission by the archbishop of Tours to take their mills on the Loire above or below the islands and sluices of the canons of Saint Maurice but not to fasten them to the bank belonging to the canons.[27] There were many disadvantages to floating mills. They were more subject to stoppage due to ice, flood or drought than were mills with sluices and mill ponds. Because of the instability and irregular movement of floating mills, their product was of a lower quality. Boat mills, if chained to a bridge, were just as harmful to it as land-based mills, and floating mills were even more of a hindrance to navigation than stationary ones.

The whole subject of medieval French boat mills is a vexed one and especially their number. However, if one classifies as floating mills only those described as *molendinum navile* or *moulins à nef* or those belonging to persons possessing the right to *voies et attaches des moulins des ponts*, as at Saumur and Orleans, and if one assumes that all *molendina terrena* and all mills possessing *unum stallum in archa pontis* or described as 'assis en l'eau de Seine'[28] were stationary mills, then the number of floating mills was considerably fewer than the land-based ones in medieval France. This conclusion should occasion no surprise. Boat mills were necessarily restricted to navigable rivers with a sufficiently strong current and were unable to adjust, through the use of overshot wheels, chutes, sluices and mill ponds, to conditions of drought or flood.

In at least two cases in the twelfth and thirteenth centuries floating mills were superseded by land-based ones. One of these examples occurred on the Agout, a tributary of the Tarn, in the seneschalcy of Toulouse, where in 1267 a knight complained that whereas others had been allowed to replace their boat mills by stationary ones, he had been forbidden to do so.[29] The other case was at Toulouse.

At Toulouse in the twelfth century there were a large number of floating mills; but even the considerable drop of the Garonne at this point seems to have been inadequate, and in 1177 the millers obtained from the prior of Sainte-Marie-de-la-Daurade permission to build a *chaussée* crossing the river obliquely and ending at the right abutment of the Pont Neuf, also called the Daurade Bridge. This *chaussée* consisted of two parallel sets of driven piles, the space between them being filled with dirt and gravel to form a dam. Neither boatmen nor bridge owners can have felt happy about the *chaussée*. Such a mill dam, when open, must have caused scouring of bridge piers. As for the boatmen, although the prior had been ordered to leave a passage for them, they were obliged to go into court to force him to open the dam.[30] After the construction of the *chaussée* the floating mills were superseded by stationary ones. Although boat mills were cheaper to build than land ones, they were unacceptable to boatmen for they blocked the passage of streams and had to be moved to let vessels pass. Bridge owners found that floating mills sometimes slipped their moorings and rammed piers. Boat mills were subject to shipwreck and difficult of access as frequently the grain could only be brought to the mill by boat. Perhaps the demands of boat traffic and the preservation of bridges had something to do with the conversion at Toulouse from floating mills to stationary ones, but G. Sicard has offered a more probable explanation. Since after the change Toulouse's needs were supplied by fewer mills, she attributes it to the superior efficiency of land-based mills.

Boat mills have been reported for the medieval period not only at Toulouse but also at Avignon, Lyons, Ponts-de-Cé, Orleans and Paris, but it is doubtful that at this time there were any at Paris. The belief that there were boat mills at Paris in the Middle Ages seems to rest on the statements of nineteenth- and twentieth-century writers. The case for floating mills attached to the Grand Pont was made in 1837 when G. D. Depping, in publishing Etienne Boileau's thirteenth-century *Règlemens sur les arts et métiers de Paris*, misread a word in the statutes of the millers of the Grand Pont. The passage in question was 'Li Meunier de Grand Pont ne puet desliener (deslieuer) nului'. Depping read the sentence to mean that the millers could not *deslieuer*, that is, untie anything, which he took to be a boat mill.[31] However, R. de Lespinasse and François Bonnardot insisted that the word *deslieuer* cannot be derived from Low Latin and does not fit the context whereas *desliener* does, so that the text should read, 'The millers of the Grand Pont cannot refuse to grind for anyone'.[32] Lespinasse's and Bonnardot's reading and translation have been accepted by the standard dictionaries of Old French of Godefroy and Tobler-Lommatzsch.[33] Some historians of milling, not finding later evidence for floating mills at the Grand Pont, have supposed that they disappeared in the great flood of 1296.[34]

An illustration in the *Life of Saint Denis* where mills are shown, one under each of three arches of a bridge (Fig. 2), has sometimes been considered as evidence for floating mills at Paris.[35] However, this interpretation will not pass muster. A careful examination of the picture will demonstrate that the mill bears little or no resemblance to the types of floating mills in use in the seventeenth century. The later ones are all built low with a mill house in a boat. In the *Life of Saint Denis* the boat is in front of the mill house, which is raised up on piles and reached by a ladder, and in any case the boat is much too small to carry the mill house. There is no boat supporting either end of the wheel; one end is fixed in the masonry of the pier and the other is under the platform supporting the mill stones and hopper.[36] Writing in the twentieth century, Charles Duplomb in his *Histoire générale des ponts de Paris* asserted that in the fifteenth century the mills below the Pont-Notre-Dame were placed on boats, but his only evidence was that this was 'according to custom'.[37]

If there were no floating mills at Paris in the Middle Ages it could not have been a question of an inadequate flow or insufficient drop.[38] Rather, congestion of the Seine at Paris was extreme and the river was tightly controlled by the *Marchandise de l'eau* and by the convent of Sainte-Magloire. Householders, in building their homes extending out from bridges, were admonished to avoid encroaching on the channel of the *Marchandise de l'eau*.[39] Almost every mill had its individual race, but permission to drive as much as a single pile had to be secured from the convent of Saint-Magloire, which owned the river bed between the Ile-Saint-Louis and the Grand Pont. There were acrimonious disputes requiring official adjudication as to which convent's mill race was one foot over into the water of another.[40] In the thirteenth century it was obligatory for merchants descending the Seine to take aboard a pilot to guide the boat safely through the master arch of the Grand Pont, avoiding the piles of mill races, walkways and houses. Penalties for ramming piles, buildings and bridges were severe. By the fifteenth century boats ascending the Seine were also required to take on board a pilot.[41]

By the seventeenth century the situation at Paris had changed and there were boat mills on the Seine at this point. There was no longer an abbey of Saint-Magloire with its restrictive practices, but whether the two facts were connected is unclear. Seventeenth-century pictures show floating mills at Paris, both the type with the mill wheel hung between two boats and the type with two water wheels, one on either side of the boat. The latter sort was identified with the capital of France, for in the eighteenth century Antoine de la Pluche in his *Spectacle de la Nature* gave an illustration of a floating mill 'after the mills of Paris'.[42]

At Orleans there were both stationary and floating mills. There were mills on piles in the ducal arch and one next to the right bank, but there seem to have been far more boat mills above and below the bridge. In the latter case they were fastened to the bridge by chains. In October 1428 the English, besieging Orleans, sank with cannon balls and bombards a dozen boat mills upstream from the new tower.[43] Despite the fact that each floating mill at the bridge at Orleans had the right to a specific location, they were not converted into stationary mills. It should have been cheaper to place a mill on a boat than to build a mill house, but perhaps a more important consideration at Orleans was that the erection of a mill house would have meant driving piles into the river bed to support the structure. At Orleans the bed of the Loire is full of springs, and piles, supposed to be driven until they refused the ram, disappeared into the sandy bottom. When it was a question of rebuilding the bridge at Orleans in 1436, the Orléanais had more than one anxious consultation about secure foundations.[44] Even in the eighteenth century Perronet, armed with ample funds, improved technology and inexhaustible manpower, had great difficulties driving piles deeply enough to support the piers of the new bridge.[45] It is no wonder if medieval inhabitants of Orleans preferred to avoid pile-driving.

DAMAGE TO BRIDGES FROM MILLS

Millers were intensely interested in an adequate volume of water for mill operation and to procure it they frequently resorted to the construction of dams, sluices and water gates. Placing a mill below a masonry bridge could result in an accelerated flow for improved operation, and at some places the piers were pressed into service as part of a mill dam, thus reducing the costs of its construction. Massive stone piers supporting houses, shops and chapels cut off a substantial portion of the freeway, but nevertheless frequently the hopes of millers for a swift current were disappointed. Take the case at Orleans. There the mills at the bridge were situated on either side of the great arch kept open for navigation at that part of the bridge between the Châtelet in the city and the island, the Motte Saint-Antoine. Between these points the bridge piers obstructed approximately a quarter of the river. The distance between the Châtelet and the Motte Saint-Antoine was about 92 m and the remains of the medieval bridge, demolished in 1760 and measured in 1866, showed the sums of the widths of the piers to have been about 22 m.[46] Yet this obstruction of itself was insufficient to provide an adequate volume of water flowing rapidly enough to allow boats and mills to operate on a river like the Loire, where at Orleans in the summertime navigation ceased and it was possible to walk dry shod over much of the river bed.

The solution to the problem of enough water appeared to millers to be dams and mill races. At Orleans there was built a submersible dam called a *duit* crossing the Loire obliquely from the Sologne bank to the Motte Saint-Antoine to direct the flow to the navigable arch and the mills at the bridge. At some places if the masonry piers of a medieval bridge did not assure an ample current for mill operation they could nevertheless be made part of a *chaussée*. Such was the case in the thirteenth century at Saint-Quentin. In 1237 the monks of Saint-Quentin-en-l'Isle made an agreement with the people of the town whereby the commune promised to maintain three arches of the bridge, and the convent was allowed to place planks in the arches as sluice gates above its mill. Objections by the townspeople that the water gates might cause flooding were met when the monks installed three rods to measure the height of the water and agreed to open the gates whenever the water reached a certain mark.[47] At Saint-Quentin the monks, by blocking all of the arches of the stream, had converted it into a mill race. There were also dams across the river at Toulouse and at La Ferté-Milon (Aisne),[48] but it was more usual merely to pre-empt one or two arches of a bridge for this purpose and to reserve one or more for navigation.

Bridge owners saw mills and mill dams as causing scouring and increasing the menace of floods. The magnified threat of floods from the construction of dams or blocking of arches by mills does not seem to have disturbed mill owners, whether at Saint-Quentin, at Orleans or at the Grand Pont of Paris. At Orleans the submersible dam was undoubtedly responsible in February 1435 for the force with which the rampaging waters of the Loire descended on that part of the bridge between the Motte Saint-Antoine and the town of Orleans, carrying away six arches as well as five houses on the bridge. The one arch left standing, the second from the town, was that in which the ducal mills were located.

At Paris the severity of the damage to the Grand Pont in the flood of 1296 seems to have been at least partly due to the intransigence of certain mill owners. At the Grand Pont in the thirteenth century ten of the eleven arches to the north of the great arch were reserved for navigation and three arches to the south of it were each blocked by a mill.[49] During the flood of December 1280 two arches of the Grand Pont were swept away and it is probable that damage would have been greater had not King Philip IV ordered the demolition of two mills just to the north of the master arch. These belonged to the chapters of Saint-Merry and Sainte-Opportune, and they insisted on the re-establishment of the mills despite the risk to the bridge. When the king was reluctant, the chapters obtained ecclesiastical sanctions; that is, the cessation of divine service by the cathedral chapter of Paris and ultimately the intervention of the pope.[50] Accordingly the mills were rebuilt, and it is perhaps not surprising that in 1296 a more severe flood ruined both the Grand Pont and the mills below it.

Bridge owners not only had reason to complain of mills because of their role in increasing flood damage: they also contributed to the undermining of piers. The greatest single challenge confronting medieval bridge builders was the construction of stable piers, a peculiarly difficult problem for them to solve with their limited resources of technological knowledge, finances and manpower. Unfortunately the operation of mill wheels and the opening of mill races caused scouring, tending to wash away foundations. This hazard to bridges from mills was recognized as early as the twelfth century. At Agen in 1189 the placing of mills too near the bridge was prohibited. A charter of Richard the Lionheart allowed the inhabitants of Agen to solicit alms for bridge construction, provided that no mill nor anything else that could cause the bridge to deteriorate should be built within five ells (about 6 m) of it.[51] A similar prohibition appears in the charter in which Eudes de Sully, bishop of Paris, in 1205 allowed the abbot and convent of Saint-Maur-des Fossées to build a bridge at Saint-Maur. Permission was given but precluded the building of anything 'nec in ponte nec in pontis appendicibus' whereby the bridge might be damaged. Mills were expressly forbidden.[52] About the same time, in 1203, the lord of Beaugency, giving to Notre-Dame de Beaugency a place for a mill in the fifth arch of the bridge over the Loire, counting from the castle, specified that the mill should not harm the bridge.[53]

Actual damage was done to the bridges at Ponts-de-Cé[54] and at Orleans by floating mills. The accounts of 'the bridge at Orleans and the hospital situated on the said bridge' for 1387–9 contain a payment to a sergeant of the Châtelet for notifying the owners of the *Moulin de Mardereau* that it must be removed because it was damaging the bridge. Nothing was done so, according to the same accounts, a second sergeant was sent.[55] The next we hear is that in 1405 a diver verified the damage to the bridge caused by a floating mill belonging to the Maison-Dieu and that this mill and the *Moulin de Mardereau* were removed.[56] There nevertheless continued to be floating mills at the Orleans bridge. For reasons similar to those of the bridge wardens at Orleans the consuls of Avignon in 1485 brought suit against Bernard de Béarn, formerly master of the ports of Villeneuve-lès-Avignon, accusing him of having attached in 1480 a mill on boats to the principal pier of the Pont-Saint-Bénézet, specifically to the arch where most boats passed.[57] The consuls claimed that eddies caused by the mill wheel undermined the pier foundations and that the presence of the floating mill rendered the spot dangerous for navigation.

Conflicts of interest among bridge owners and millers continued into the modern period. In the time of Francis I a lawsuit was brought in Albi to prevent deterioration of the bridge by the mill situated on it.[58] The damage to bridges caused by mills was still going on in the eighteenth century. The king's council of state in 1746 declared that the deterioration of many bridges had been caused by the building of nearby mills, because millers constructed works to hold back the water and make it flow more rapidly at the mill wheel. This undermined the piers and occasioned damage to and sometimes the collapse of the bridge. Accordingly, the council of state ordered all titles to mills to be examined.[59] It is doubtful that much if anything was done to remedy the situation, for not much later the *Encyclopédie* in its article on mills shows the typical water mill downstream from a bridge and built between its masonry piers.[60] As long as millers benefited from a location at a bridge, whether because of easy access, decreased construction costs or an accelerated flow of water, they were almost certain to build mills there, whether or not they damaged the bridge.

Mills and Boatmen

In medieval France mills seem to have been little affected by opposition from those maintaining bridges, but it was otherwise with boatmen, who had the means of making their dissatisfaction felt. Of three groups vitally interested in the waterways of France, millers, bridge owners and boatmen, only the last was organized to protect its interests. Along the Seine the Hanse of Paris, also called the *Marchandise de l'eau*, and in central France the *Communauté des Marchands fréquentant la Loire et les fleuves descendant en icelle* gained royal support in their efforts to maintain a navigable channel. Although along the Loire ascent was under sail, along the Seine the maintenance of satisfactory towpaths was of the first importance. Here the *Marchandise de l'eau* was on the alert for encroachments by mills.

The association of mills with bridges compounded the difficulties of boatmen because it increased obstruction of the waterway. It was typical of medieval French bridges that only one or two arches should be open for navigation. The others were occupied by mills or blocked by mill dams. For example, at Blois there was a single arch for the passage of boats and there was a stone cross on it so it could easily be identified by boatmen.[61] At Sens in 1313 there were three arches kept open for navigation and a document of that year, in which the king of France gave permission to the Dean and Chapter of Sens to install mills under the arches of the bridge, forbade them to make a dam above or below the three arches reserved for boats.[62] At the bridge at Joigny one of the four streams into which the Yonne was divided was set aside after 1330 for the passage of boats and two served as mill streams, one for a small mill on the second arch and one for a large mill on the eighth arch.[63]

In cases where there was only one navigable arch, a flood could block navigation entirely. This happened at Orleans after the great inundations of 1435 when the navigable arch collapsed into the Loire. The solitary arch still standing between the Motte Saint-Antoine and the Châtelet, the part of the river where the mills were situated and where the boats passed, was the arch of the ducal mills with its mills on piles. The distress of the boatmen, denied a channel through the bridge, seems not to have affected the people of Orleans. Apparently they considered the bridge merely as a passage from one river bank to the other, except that, of course, it was a convenient place to collect tolls for bridge maintenance from the boats passing underneath. The Community of Merchants frequenting the Loire and its tributaries was obliged to go into court to force the bridge commissioners to remove the piles blocking the arch of the duke's mills. Only then could navigation on the Loire past Orleans resume.[64]

One of the reasons millers were attracted to bridges as a site for their mills was that relatively little expense in building dams could procure them the swift current they delighted in. This same rapidity of flow was a hazard to navigation. Bridges and mills were a recognized cause of shipwreck for which the Community of Merchants frequenting the Loire was willing to pay an indemnity. Records have survived for the years 1492–4, 1502–4 and

1534–7: out of seventy-two shipwrecks eleven occurred at bridges known to have mills at them.[65]

MILL RACES AND NAVIGATION

There was considerable friction between millers, who preferred to dam the stream, and boatmen, in whose interests it was vital it be kept open. This was true both in England[66] and France. For example, at La Ferté-Milon (Aisne), arrondissement Château-Thierry, canton Neuilly-Saint-Front, the monks of Bourgfontaine, some time after 1349, sued those of Saint-Jean-des-Vignes of Soissons for the right to have their fishing-boats pass through the mill race at the bridge, where the convent of Saint-Jean had a mill wheel, 'estant et tournant en la rivière d'Ourcq'.[67] It was possible to compromise between the disputing parties, the millers and boatmen, by arranging the sluice to funnel a large volume of water to the mill wheel, in which case no water gate was needed.[68] Certainly the submersible dam at Orleans performed this function and on this point for once the interests of millers and boatmen coincided. However, most mill races probably had water gates. It was evidently common for boats to pass through sluices, as above Troyes on the Seine in 1388.[69] At Les Régennes (Yonne), commune Appoigny, the bishop of Auxerre promised in 1145 always to keep open for boats the sluice of his mill beyond the bridge.[70] Similarly, at Cheny (Yonne), canton Seignelay, before 1185 the abbot of Saint-Remy of Auxerre was permitted to build two mills on the Yonne, one next to and one above the bridge, but only if he left a passage for boats one toise (1.9 m) wide.[71] Such a width cannot have accommodated the barges used on the Seine, Oise and Yonne, for the royal ordinance of 1416 declared that sluices were customarily 24 ft in width (7.92 m).[72] A glance at Fig. 1 gives an idea how it was possible for a boat to pass through a mill race without harm to the water wheel.

There were numerous complaints against millers who failed to open their water gates, overcharged for passage through their sluices or allowed their mill races to deteriorate and become a hindrance to navigation. Thus the bishop of Auxerre was ordered by the king's government in 1269 and again in 1379 to restore his sluice to its former state since boatmen charged that he had narrowed it.[73]

Boatmen may frequently have found the cost of passing through mill races exorbitant, but at least they represented navigable water. The sluice of Combarbès, formerly near Vernon, is described by the ordinance of 1416 as 'where the boats, loaded or empty, pass, especially when the waters are low'.[74] Evidently millers, impounding water, had some when the rest of the stream was suffering from drought. At another place, if the merchants needed to pass a ford the miller was obliged to open his water gate and leave it open until they had passed the ford.[75] The millers, on the other hand, regretted the loss of water as it prevented them from grinding. In the fifteenth century during the controversy over making the Eure navigable above Nogent-le-Roi, proponents of the project insisted that the mill race filled up in half an hour after the passage of boats, but millers contended that they frequently were unable to grind for a whole day until the water level had recovered.[76]

Mill races could offer advantages to boats over and beyond that of providing navigable water. They could facilitate the passage of boats upstream under a bridge. On the Seine, Oise and Yonne, barges were pulled upstream by horses. However, commonly the solitary navigable arch was in the middle of the stream where the channel was deepest, and to pass the boats safely through this arch was the duty of the master of the arch or pilot. At Villeneuve-sur-Yonne (Yonne), arrondissement of Joigny (formerly Villeneuve-le Roi), the pilot was pilot not only of the bridge but also of the mill race below it. He was obliged to have a rowboat large enough to carry four barrels of wine, this size being necessary so that when the waters were high his little boat would be adequate to carry the necessary cables and lines. In addition to the boat, he was required to maintain at his own expense a varlet and an *indart* or *hindart* or *aindar*, a winch turned *à force de gens*, 'by manpower when the waters are so strong [*fort*] that it is necessary in passing these boats' beyond the bridge.[77] The mill race was below the bridge, which crossed an island, and the *hindart*, according to the *Ordonnances*, was on a mound on this island and above the bridge. Accordingly, it should have been easy to get a straight pull for the windlass, at least once the boat was in the arch. The pilot was to go in his boat, accompanied by his varlet, to meet boats ascending the Yonne, receive the lines and ropes from the boatmen and tie the boat to the iron rings inside the arch. It is unclear whether fastening the boat to the arch was merely so it could withstand the force of the current when the water gate was opened and the pilot immediately tied the cables to the windlass or whether the boatmen, by wrapping the ropes around a cleat, moved the boat upstream and warped it alongside the interior of the arch, and then the *indart* pulled the boat upstream. In any case, in the final operation the pilot returned the lines to the carriers, now above the bridge, the cables were once more fastened to the horses and the boat proceeded upstream.

It seems to have been only on mill races that these windlasses were situated and only in the department of the Yonne. They were mostly at or near Auxerre, about 44 km from Villeneuve-sur-Yonne. The winches were owned, for example, by the bishop of Auxerre, who had a mill race below the bridge, by the chapter and by the monks of Saint-Marien. There was an *hindart* at Auxerre as early as 1207, but the use of windlasses to pull boats upstream does not seem to have spread beyond the department of the Yonne. Boatmen passing up and down the Yonne must have been well-acquainted with windlasses, which were cheaper for them than employing extra horses and men. The fee paid to the pilot of the bridge and sluice at Villeneuve-sur-Yonne was the same, whether the waters were high or low, whereas merchants paid more for every extra horse and man employed for towing boats on the Seine above Rouen. Apart from local resistance to change and opposition to the restriction of employment opportunities, the fact that the windlass was not more widely used may be accounted for by its inadaptability. It was useful only under a limited set of conditions, including a secure position directly upstream from the arch or water gate so as to ensure a straight pull.

The compensations in the existence of mill races seem to have been little appreciated by boatmen. They regularly carried their grievances to the king's government, and in the fourteenth and fifteenth centuries the provost of the *Marchands de l'eau* ordered the demolition of any mill dam on the Seine or its tributaries which was harmful to navigation. His sergeants aggressively carried out his orders to the indignation of millers.

FLOATING MILLS

If boatmen detested mill dams, they were equally unhappy about floating mills. Millers sought out the deepest and swiftest part of the stream for their boat mills, a practice which brought them into competition with bargemen conveying freight. At Orleans, as at Toulouse and Avignon, the water-power requirements of floating mills and the needs of boatmen came into conflict. In 1233 because a boat mill belonging to the *domus pauperum* obstructed traffic in the navigable arch at Orleans, Queen Ingeborg gave the *domus* an arch of the bridge next to the arch housing the royal (later the ducal) mills.[78]

At Toulouse and at Orleans the problem of boat mills was resolved in favour of the boatmen, but the case of the floating mills at Lyons was different. They remained an intractable problem for centuries. There were floating mills at Lyons at least from the fifteenth into the nineteenth century, and they were on the Rhone, not the Saône, where there was insufficient fall to operate them.[79] When we first hear complaints about mills, they were upstream from the Pont-de-la-Guillotière. Its enormous piers, 8, 10 and 12 m thick,[80] acted as a partial dam so that there must have been an ample supply of water above the bridge. In 1421 the boatmen who supplied Lyons with wood demanded that the mills in the town fishpond be moved to a place where they would not hamper navigation.[81] In vain the millers offered to recompense the boatmen for any losses they incurred. The boatmen appealed to the consuls of Lyons, who decided that the mills should be located where they could best grind, because they were more necessary to the commonwealth than the boatmen and it would be a great inconvenience to have the mills at a distance. The boatmen hauled the millers into the king's court of Roanne. The court decision is not recorded in the consular registers of Lyons, but in the seventeenth century the mills were downstream from the bridge and in the eighteenth they had been relegated to a point south of Lyons, where the Saône and Rhone meet.[82]

However, the exile of the floating mills to a point below the city remote from their former station at the Pont-de-la-Guillotière solved neither of Lyons' two problems: how to assure a dependable supply of flour and how to prevent the boat mills from hindering navigation. The Academy of Lyons offered a prize on the following topic: To determine what is the construction most advantageous for the product and least harmful to navigation of mills on a river.[83] The award was made in 1763 to M. Du Bost, a merchant dealing in embroidery. A book inspired by the offer of the prize contains much information on the situation at Lyons: Edme Béguillet, *Traité de la Connoissance générale des grains et de la mouture* (Paris, 1775). M. Béguillet takes the viewpoint of a lawyer rather than of an engineer or of a technician. He assures us that at Lyons the floating mills are necessarily in the middle of the Rhone, because at the edge of the river the current is too slow for mills. They cannot be placed one behind another in a straight line, because in that case the first would cut off the current so that the second would be, as it were, in a lake, unable to operate. Therefore, the second is set a little beyond the first, and the third a little farther out than the second, so that when fourteen or fifteen mills are in place they pre-empt a considerable portion of the Rhone. It is so dangerous for boats to pass the mills at Lyons that passengers on the public river boats prefer to embark and disembark below the mills despite the inconveniently great distance from the city. The situation is made worse by the professional pride of the pilots, who feel that safely passing the mills of Lyons is a master stroke.[84] Hardly a year passes without a shipwreck, and M. Béguillet cites a recent disaster in which eighty-five to a hundred people drowned.

The floating mills at Lyons were of the two-boat type and M. Dubost, in winning the prize, had proposed the substitution of a smaller, single-boat, two-wheel type as less of a nuisance to navigation. This was the less efficient of the two types of floating mills, which were less productive than stationary ones anyway. However, historians of technology do not need to be reminded that the efficiency of a machine is only one of several factors determining its adoption. Thus after the Middle Ages in France the number of boat mills greatly increased despite the known facts of their inferior product and lower productivity, the inconvenience of operation and the risks of shipwreck. None of these factors was decisive in procuring the banning of boat mills by the royal government in 1844. It was the interference with river traffic which moved the boatmen to effect their abolition.

What brought bridge owners, millers and boatmen together was the stream; what divided them was the uses to which it should be put. Bridge owners saw the stream as demanding the construction of a safe passage across it; millers considered it a source of power; the boatmen as a means of navigation. An occasional mill race was useful to boatmen, whether as collecting enough water to ensure passage of boats or as making ascent cheaper through the use of windlasses, but under most circumstances mills added to the expense, delays and perils of boatmen. Bridges benefited mills because of easier access, a swifter current and a larger clientele but, for bridges, mills were a source of scouring and undermining of piers and of increasing losses from floods due to extra congestion on the river. Bridge owners seem to have thought of boatmen chiefly as a source of customs duties to contribute to repairs, but navigation was made much more dangerous by the hazards of passing under the arches of bridges. In the late medieval and early modern periods it was the boatmen who were in the ascendancy. They had the active support of the royal government in restricting the use of mills and in improving navigation. Perhaps even more than mills, medieval bridges suffered from this new programme. In the fifteenth century, for example, the king sponsored the extension of navigable stretches along the Eure and Seine rivers, and in the sixteenth and seventeenth centuries extensive works in the canalization of rivers were undertaken. Levees along the banks of rivers raised the flood level so high that the medieval bridges over the Loire were unable to accommodate the new crests. Almost all of them were washed out and had to be replaced. On the Rhone in the nineteenth century two arches of the venerable Pont-Saint-Espirit were replaced by one, higher, steel arch to allow steam boats to ascend the river even at times of high water.[85] In the 1850s the city of Lyons was still being threatened with famine because of a shortage of flour, but not because of the inadequate functioning of floating mills at the city. Navigational problems were preventing flour from reaching Lyons.

Notes

1. Procopius, *History of the Wars*, Book V (The Gothic War), XIX, 19–20 (Loeb ed., 3, 190, 1919).

2. *Marii episcopi Aventicensis chronica: CCCCLV-DLXXXI. Mon. Ger. Hist. Auctores antiquissimi*, Vol. 2, Part 2, p. 237: Berlin, 1894.

3. Lasteyrie du Saillant, Robert Charles, Count of, ed., *Cartulaire général de Paris, ou recueil de documents relatifs à l'histoire et topographie de Paris*, Paris, 1887, No. 45. Anne Lombard-Jourdain, *Paris: genèse de la 'ville'. La rive droite de la Seine des origines à 1223*, Institut de Recherche et d'Histoire des Textes, Paris, 1876, pp. 38ff.

4. Gustave Fagniez, *Etudes sur l'industrie et la classe industrielle à Paris et au XIIIe et au XIVe siècle*, Bibl. Ecole Hautes-Etudes, 33, Paris, 1877, p. 166, n. 2.

5. A. Terroine and L. Fossier, eds., *Chartes et documents de l'abbaye de Saint-Magloire*, Vol. II, 1280–1330. Documents, études et repertoires publiés par l'Institut de Recherche et d'Histoire des Textes, 2 : 113, No. 84, 1 May 1296 and 2 : 324, No. 234 in 1317.

6. Fagniez, as note 4, p. 161, n. 2.

7. Georges Huisman, *La Juridiction de la municipalité parisienne de Saint Louis à Charles VII*, Bibliothèque d'Histoire de Paris, Paris, 1912, pp. 100–1.

8. Emile Epiphanus Morel, ed., *Cartulaire de Saint-Corneille de Compiègne*, Société historique de Compiègne, Montdidier, 1909, pp. 251–2. Auguste Longnon, *Dictionnaire topographique du département de la Marne comprenant les noms de lieu anciens et modernes*, Paris, 1891, s.v.

9. Eugène d'Auriac, *Histoire de l'ancienne cathédrale et des évêques d'Alby, depuis les premiers temps connus jusqu'à la fondation de la nouvelle église Sainte-Cécile*, Paris, 1858, pp. 203–4.

10. Alexandre Collin, *Le Pont des Tourelles à Orléanais (1120–1760). Etude sur les ponts aux moyen-âge*, Mémoires de la Société historique et archéologique de l'Orléanais, 26, Orleans, 1895, p. 435.

11. Alexandre Pougeois, *L'Antique et Royale Cité de Moret-sur-Loing (Seine-et-Marne)*, Paris, 1875, p. 31. Illustration at back.

12. Collin, as note 10, p. 248.

13. Auguste Vidal, ed., *Douze Computes consulaires d'Albi du XIVe siècle*, Archives historiques de l'Albigeois, fasc. 9, 2, Albi, 1911, pp. 235–9.

14. G. Vignat, ed., *Cartulaire de l'abbaye de Notre-Dame de Beaugency*, Mémoires de la Société historique et archéologique de l'Orléanais, 1, Orleans, 1879, No. 127, p. 146.

15. Maurice Prou, *Recueil des actes de Philippe I, roi de France (1059–1108)*, Chartes et diplômes relatifs à l'histoire de France au moyen-âge, 1, Paris, 1908, No. LIII, p. 143.

16. Augustin Fliche, *Le Règne de Philippe Ier, roi de France (1060–1108)*, Paris, 1912, p. 126. See also Paul Quesvers, 'Les Ponts de Montereau-Fault-Yonne (Suite)' in *Annales de la Société historique et archéologique du Gâtinais*, 5 (1887). On p. 233 the mills are called 'sur le pont', but on pp. 241, 245 they are described as below the bridge. On the Yonne one mill was behind, i e. downstream from, the other.

17. On this point see the discussion of Terry Scott Reynolds, *Science and the Water Wheel: the Development and Diffusion of Theoretical and Experimental Doctrines relating to the Vertical Water Wheel, c. 1500–c. 1850*, unpublished dissertation, University of Kansas, pp. 59–63.

18. Fagniez, as note 4, p. 163.

19. *Chartes . . . Saint-Magloire*, 2 : 606–608, No. 397 In 1299. The list is printed in Fagniez, as note 4, p. 157, n. 1, together with other lists. L. H. Labande, 'Inventaire du château de Vaucluse (1414)' in *Annales d'Avignon*, 1 (1912), pp. 63–5.

20. Bernard Forest de Bélidor, *Architecture hydraulique, ou l'Art de conduire, d'élever et de ménager les eaux pour des différens besoins de la vie*, Paris, 1737–53, Vol. I, Book II, p. 297. He notes that the slots in the lantern wheel should be at least 18 in high (45.9 cm) so that the wheel should not be damaged by the current.

21. Maximilien Quantin, 'Histoire de la rivière d'Yonne' in *Bulletin de la Société des Sciences historiques et naturelles de l'Yonne*, 39, 1885, p. 400. F. Lot, 'Mélanges carolin-giennes: Le pont de Pîtres', *Le Moyen-Age*, 18, 1905, p. 23.

22. On the Brandywine, near Wilmington, Delaware, the Duponts built a series of water mills in the early nineteenth century. In the eighteenth century at the Bazacle mills at Toulouse, one horizontal water wheel drove several mill stones, but I have not found evidence that this practice was in use in France in the Middle Ages.

23. R. J. Forbes, 'Power' in *A History of Technology*, ed. C. Singer *et al.*, London, 1957, Vol. 2, p. 607, Fig. 551.

24. S. Gagnière, 'Les Moulins à bateaux sur le Rhône à Avignon et dans les environs' in *Provence historique*, 1, 1950, p. 75.

25. For pictures of each type see Marcel Arpin, *Historique de la meunerie et la boulangerie depuis les temps préhistoriques jusqu'à l'année 1914*, 1, Paris, 1948, Figs. 13, 14.

26. Noël Antoine Pluche, *Spectacle de la Nature or Nature Display'd being Discourses on such Particulars of Natural History as were thought the most proper to excite the Curiosity and form the Mind of Youth*, trans. from the original French, 3rd edition, 5, London, 1753, p. 321, Pl. IX, X. J. A. Borgnis, *Traité complet de mécanique appliquée aux arts, contenant l'Exposition méthodique des théories et des expériences les plus utiles pour diriger le choix, l'invention, la construction et l'emploi de toutes les espèces de machines*, Vol. 1, Paris, 1819, pp. 59–60.

27. Charles Loizeau de Grandmaison, *Inventaire-sommaire des archives départementales antérieures à 1790*, Vol. 3 Archives ecclésiastiques, Series H. Clergé regulier, Tours, 1891, p. 73.

28. Albert Lecoy de la Marche, ed., *Extraits des comptes et mémoriaux du roi René, pour servir à l'histoire des arts au XVe siècle; publiés d'après les originaux des archives nationales*, Paris, 1873, No. 440, p. 159. On 24 August 1468 King René gave the right to attach mills to the bridges over the Loire and Vienne at Saumur to the abbey of Saint-Florent of Saumur. There has been a tendency to assume that medieval French mills were almost all boat mills. See G. Rivals, 'Floating Mills in France. A few Notes on History, Technology and the Lives of Men' in *The International Molinological Society. Transactions, Third Symposium*, Netherlands, 6–11 May 1973, pp. 147–58. Fagniez

states the mills were moored to the Grand Pont on the downstream side, but the mill of Saint-Magloire was described soon after the flood of 1296 as 'sis en aval du Grand Pont' in *Chartes ... Saint-Magloire*, II, No. 397, 606. Arpin, as note 25, I, 23 and Fagniez, as note 4, p. 162 refer to mills moored at the Rue de la Tannerie and to the pont des Planches de Mibray, but the *Chartes ... de Saint-Magloire* describe only stationary mills at these points.

29. Auguste Molinier, ed., *Correspondance administrative d'Alphonse de Poitiers*, 1894–1900, Collection de documents inédits, I, 184, No. 298.

30. Germain Sicard, *Aux Origines des sociétés anonymes. Les moulins de Toulouse au moyen âge*, Ecole pratique des Hautes Etudes, VIe sec., 5, Paris, 1953, pp. 38–9.

31. Etienne Boileau, *Règlemens sur les arts et métiers de Paris, redigés au 13e siècle et commu sous le nom du Livre des métiers d'Etienne Boileau*, publiés avec des notes par G. H. Depping, Paris, 1837, Collection des documents inédits sur l'histoire de France, 4, 19.

32. Etienne Boileau, *Les Métiers et corporations de la ville de Paris. XIIIe siècle. Le livre des métiers d'Etienne Boileau*, ed. René Lespinasse and François Bonnardot, Histoire générale de Paris, Paris, 1879, pp. 16, 317.

33. Frédéric Godefroy, *Dictionnaire de l'ancienne langue française et de tous ses dialectes du IXe au XVe siècle*, Paris, 1880–1902, s.v. Adolf Tobler-Lommatzsch, *Altfranzösisches Wörterbuch: Adolf Toblers nachgelassene Materialien bearbeitet und mit unterstützung der Preussischen Akademie der Wissenschaften*, ed. Erhard Lommatzsch, Berlin, 1825–1971, s.v.

34. Richard Bennett and John Elton, *History of Corn Milling*, London and Liverpool, 1898–1904 Vol. 2, p. 74. Forbes, as note 23, 2, 608. See the discussion of Bradford Bennett Blaine, *The Application of Water-Power to Industry during the Middle Ages*, unpublished dissertation, University of California at Los Angeles, 1966, p. 32 n. 89.

35. Bertrand Gille, 'The Medieval Age of the West (Fifth century to 1350)' in *A History of Technology and Invention*, ed. Maurice Daumas, Vol. 1, p. 452, Fig. 35. Forbes, as note 23, 2, 608. Rivals, as note 28, p. 150.

36. Bennett and Elton describe, Vol. 2, p. 74, the mills as built on piles or esterlings beneath the arches of the bridge with small ferry boats in attendance.

37. Charles Duplomb, *Histoire générale des ponts de Paris*, Paris, 1911–13, Vol. 1, p. 203.

38. In the seventeenth century the drop between Bercy and Chaillot, a distance, according to Y. Saguet of the Service de la Navigation de la Seine, of 8,720 m, was less than a metre. See also E. Clouson, 'Les Inondations à Paris du VIe au XXe siècle' in *La Géographie*, 23, 1911, p. 93. Louis C. Hunter has informed me that such a drop would have been adequate for floating mills.

39. *Chartes ... de Saint-Magloire*, 2, 196, 5 July 1307.

40. *Ibid.*, 2, 448, 16 November 1325.

41. Huisman, as note 7, p. 34. *Ordonnances des roys de France de la troisième race, recueillies par ordre chronologique*, Paris, 1723–1849, 10, p. 323.

42. Pluche, as note 26.

43. Collin, as note 10, p. 434.

44. Archives de Loiret CC 967 f. 23 verso. See also my 'Moving ahead with the fifteenth century: new Ideas in Bridge Construction at Orleans' in *History of Technology*, 1981, pp. 12–13.

45. J. R. Perronet, *Description des projets et de la construction des ponts de Neuilly, de Mantes, d'Orleans, et d'autres*, Paris, 1782–3, Vol. 2, pp. 1ff.

46. Collin, as note 10, Atlas, 2.

47. E. Lemaire, ed., *Archives anciennes de la ville de Saint-Quentin*, Saint-Quentin, Société académique, Saint-Quentin, 1888, Vol. 1, p. 30.

48. Aimé Champollion-Figeac, *Droits et usages concernant les travaux de construction, publics ou privés sous la troisième race des rois de France*, ... (*de l'an 987 à l'an 1380*) *d'après les chartes et autres documents originaux*, reprinted from *Revue archéologique*, Paris, 1860, p. 109 after 1349, and p. 155 in 1378. The mill was a fulling mill and also used for pressing oil.

49. Fagniez, as note 4, p. 159.

50. Henri Sauval, *Histoire et recherches des antiquités de la ville de Paris*, Paris, 1724, 1, 28, p. 200.

51. G. Tholin, 'Les Ponts sur la Garonne. Extrait de l'abrégé chronologique des antiquités d'Agen par Labrunie' in *Revue de l'Agenais*, 5, 1878, p. 440.

52. Georges Bousquié, 'Histoire du pont de Saint-Maur' in *Mémoires de la Fédération des Sociétés historiques et archéologiques de Paris et de l'Ile de France*, 4, 1952, pp. 331–2.

53. *Cartulaire ... Beaugency*, as note 14.

54. Jeanne et Camille Fraysse, *Loire angevine et Maine. Mariniers et riverains d'autrefois*, Cholet, France, 1967, p. 70.

55. Archives du Loiret CC 920 f. 13 recto.

56. Collin, as note 10, pp. 432, 434.

57. Gagnière, as note 24, p. 77, n. 12.

58. E. Jolibois, 'Le Vieux Pont d'Albi' in *Revue historique, scientifique et littéraire du département du Tarn*, 11, 1878–9, p. 201.

59. E. J. M. Vigneron, *Etudes historiques sur l'administration des voies publiques aux dis-septième siècle*, 2, Paris, 1862, Pièce justificative, 320.

60. *Encyclopédie. Dictionnaire raisonné des sciences des arts et des métiers*, Vol. 10, Neufchâtel, 1865, p. 798, Pl VI.

61. Collin, as note 10, p. 209.

62. *Layettes du trésor des chartes*, ed. Alexandre Teulet, Paris, 1863–6, 1, 398b.

63. Maximilien Quantin, as note 21, p. 437. See also pp. 411, 435, 403.

64. Archives du Loiret CC 967 f. 14 verso.

65. Philippe Manteller, *Histoire de la communauté des marchands fréquentant la Loire et fleuves descendant en icelle*, Orleans, 1867–9, Vol. 1, pp. 176–7.

66. Bennett and Elton, as note 34, 2, p. 185. Reynolds, as note 17, p. 63.

67. Champollion-Figeac, as note 48.

68. There was such a mill race above the Grand Pont at Paris, and it belonged to the bishop. *Chartes .... Saint-Magloire*, 2, pp. 259ff.

69. Théophile Boutiot, 'Notice sur la navigation de la Seine et de la Barse' in *Mémoires de la Société d'Agriculture. Aube*, 2nd sér, 7, 1856, p. 76.

70. Maximilien Quantin, ed., *Cartulaire générale de l'Yonne; recueil de documents authentiques pour servir à l'histoire des pays qui forment ce département*, Société des Sciences historiques et naturelles de l'Yonne, Auxerre, 1854–60, 2, p. 394.

71. Quantin, ed., *Cartulaire général*, 2, p. 357.

72. *Ordonnances des roys de France de la troisième race, recueillies par ordre chronologique*, Paris, 1723–1849, 10, p. 342.

73. Quantin, ed., *Recueil de pièces pour faire suite au Cartulaire général de l'Yonne (XIIIe siècle)*, Auxerre, 1873, Nos. 650, 921.

74. *Ordonnances*, as note 72, 10, p. 326.

75. Godefroy, as note 33, s.v. *molinier*.

76. Claudine Billot, 'Chartres et la navigation sur l'Eure à la fin du Moyen Age', Les Transports au Moyen Age. Actes du VIIe Congrès des Médiévistes del' Enseignement supérieur, *Annales de Bretagne et des Pays de l'Quest*, 85, 1978, No. 2, p. 252.

77. *Ordonnances*, as note 72, 10, p. 339. On the question of the *hindart* or *aindar*

see Quantin, 'Histoire . . .', as note 21, p. 409. See also Quantin, ed., *Recueil*, as note 73, p. 295, No. 606.

78. Collin, as note 10, p. 434.

79. This statement was made by Edme Béguillet, *Traité de la connoissance générale des grains et de la mouture par économie, contenant la manière de moudre les grains pour en tirer une plus grande quantité de meilleur farine avec le moins de déchet, le meilleur méchanisme et la construction de diverses sortes de moulins, &c . . .*, Paris, 1775, 1, p. iv.

80. Marie-Claude Guigue, 'Notre-Dame de Lyon: recherche sur l'origine du pont de la Guillotière et du grand Hôtel-Dieu et sur l'emplacement de l'hôpital fondé à Lyon, au VIe siècle, par le roi Childebert et la reine Ultrogothe' in *Mémoires de la Société littéraire de Lyon*, 1874-5, p. 271.

81. Guigue, ed., *Registres consulaires de la ville de Lyon ou recueil des délibérations du conseil de la commerce de 1416 à 1423*, 1, Lyon, 1882, pp. 295-9.

82. Jacques-Jules Grisard, *Notice sur les plans et vues de la ville de Lyon de la fin du XVe au commencement du XVIIIe siècle*, Lyon, 1891. A view of Lyons (opposite p. 129), done by Simon Maupin in 1635, shows six floating mills, each with two boats and a water wheel between them, just downstream from the Pont du Rosne.

83. C. Emile Perret de la Menue, 'Des Moulins à blé chez les anciens, chez les modernes et particulièrement dans la ville de Lyon' in *Mémoires de la Société littéraire de Lyon*, 1867, p. 297.

84. Béguillet, as note 79, 1, p. iv.

85. M. Aymard, 'Notice sur les travaux éxécutés au pont Saint-Esprit pour la construction d'une arche marinière' in *Annales des Ponts et Chaussées*, 3rd sér., 1859, pp. 1-48.

Internal-combustion Engines and their Fuel: a Preliminary Exploration of Technological Interplay

WM. DAVID COMPTON

When underground petroleum accumulations were first exploited on a large scale in the mid-nineteenth century, it was not for their value as fuel that they were worked: petroleum was valued because it could be simply processed to yield a cheap illuminating oil. A growing shortage of plant and animal oils suitable for use in lamps, coupled with a continuing increase in demand for illuminants, assured a ready market for this material.[1] Known as 'kerosene' in the United States and as 'paraffin' in Britain, petroleum-derived lamp oil was the basis upon which great commercial empires (particularly the Standard Oil Company) were built, and until well past 1900 it remained the most valuable single product of the petroleum refinery.[2] The requirements of kerosene production dominated the technology of petroleum refining during its formative years; other components of crude petroleum were processed and marketed, but they were far less important than kerosene.

The first practical internal-combustion engine — Lenoir's gas engine — appeared about the same time as the first commercial oil wells. In 1876 Nicholas Otto's four-stroke cycle engine displaced the Lenoir and achieved commercial success in the field of small-output power units. The Otto engine normally burned town gas, but any combustible vapour would serve; and when experiments with self-propelled road vehicles began in the 1880s, the Otto engine was a logical choice for the mobile power source required.

Thanks to the properties required of lamp oil, a liquid fuel for these early automobiles was already available. Most crude petroleum contains substantial amounts of low-boiling material which, because of its volatility, often caused explosions if it was allowed to remain in lamp oil. Therefore, reputable refiners went to considerable lengths to free their illuminating oil from this volatile liquid. Known variously as 'naphtha', 'gasoline', 'benzine', or 'petroleum spirit' ('petrol'), the low-boiling part was of limited utility but amounted to a considerable fraction of crude petroleum. It was this material that the early automobile builders found readily available as the fuel for their engines.

Over a surprisingly short period, from about 1900 to 1920, the internal-combustion engine, in its applications to land and air transport, came to dominate petroleum refining — already a large and mature industry when the automobile and the airplane came into existence. The purpose of this paper is to examine the evolving relationship between the internal-combustion engine and the petroleum-refining industry which supplied the fuel for it, particularly in the United States where the development of both industries was centred.

Early Petroleum-refining Technology

The refining of crude petroleum began with separation into two to four fractions by distillation, using techniques and equipment adapted from the coal-oil industry. A typical still comprised a cylindrical cast- or wrought-iron vessel that might hold anything from a few barrels to a few hundred barrels and a water-cooled coil of pipe serving as a condenser. Even in large refineries, distillation was conducted as a batch operation. After the still was charged, a coal fire gradually brought the temperature up to the boiling point of kerosene (approximately 300°F) while the low-boiling naphtha was taken off. Kerosene was then collected as long as the specific gravity of the condensate was within the range generally recognized as suitable for lamp oil. Major refiners then distilled gas-oil and fuel oil up to 700° or 800°F, and extracted lubricants from the still residues; small independent operators usually did not.[3]

Depending upon the composition of the crude oil, such a distillation yielded perhaps 5 to 15 per cent of the original charge as naphtha, 30 to 40 per cent as kerosene and the rest as heavy distillates and residue. Since petroleum is a mixture of many closely-related chemical compounds with overlapping boiling ranges, efficient separation was not possible by simple single-stage distillation and it was necessary to redistill the kerosene fraction to remove the explosive naphtha it still contained. Chemical treatment of the kerosene followed to remove coloured and odoriferous impurities and chemically-reactive contaminants which formed gummy deposits during storage.

For the first fifty years petroleum refining consisted almost entirely of the physical separation of crude oil into fractions suitable for specific end uses, and little thought was given to chemical alteration of its components. The major exception was thermal decomposition, recognized since 1855 and practised—sometimes unwittingly—by most refiners. Coal-oil refiners knew that prolonged heating of high-boiling coal-oil fractions produced substances boiling in the kerosene range, and Downer's Kerosene Oil Company of Boston held the rights to a patent (issued in 1860) covering this process, which was known as 'cracking'. Pioneer petroleum refiners found that the yield of kerosene could be increased substantially by heating the heavy still-residues until they turned to coke. Excessive heating gave a badly contaminated product that required much more drastic chemical treatment; but if carefully done, cracking could add to the yield of kerosene without disproportionately increasing the cost of refining.[4]

Petroleum naphtha, which could amount to a quarter of the volume of the kerosene, was virtually worthless to the small refiner and hazardous into the bargain; in the oil-producing regions it was frequently dumped into the nearest creek. Large refiners sometimes redistilled the naphtha, separating it into two or more fractions which were marketed as solvents or as fuel for small portable heaters. In 1900, American refiners produced nearly 7 million barrels of naphtha, compared to 30 million barrels of kerosene.[5]

The Impact of the Motor Car

Although several hundred vehicles had been built in the 1890s, at the turn of the century the automobile could hardly be considered a serious contender for leadership in the field of private transport. Sir Harry Ricardo, one of Britain's pioneer internal-combustion engineers, recalled the typical motor car of this period as 'a rich man's fascinating but wayward toy with which one played but with little hope of reaching one's destination'.[6] As long as this was true, it is hardly surprising that petroleum refiners did not perceive the implications of the dawning automotive age for their industry.[7]

But for Henry Ford, the refiners might have gone their complacent way for many more years. Ford's concept of a simple, reliable, utilitarian vehicle priced within the reach of a large fraction of the population, however, was revolutionary in any frame of reference; and after 1908 the concept became a reality. By 1915 the United States had 2.5 million registered motor vehicles of all types,[8] and although they used only half the nation's output of gasoline,[9] some in the petroleum industry foresaw a fuel shortage. There was ample justification for this view, for while between 1900 and 1916 the number of motor vehicles registered in the United States doubled approximately every two years,[10] domestic crude oil production increased only sixfold over the entire period.[11] Throughout the nineteenth century, refiners had met increases in demand by expanding their facilities and increasing refinery throughputs; but this traditional response was clearly inadequate to keep pace with the phenomenal growth in automobile production. Until new sources of crude could fill the gap, refiners had to modify their practices however they could to meet the growing demand for motor fuel.

The problem was attacked in several ways. Improved stills were introduced which, although they did not increase the proportion of any particular fraction, increased refining capacity and reduced operating costs. A substantial addition to the gasoline supply was made by 'widening the cut' — raising the end-point temperature of the gasoline fraction from about 280°F (140°C) to somewhat over 400°F (250°C), thereby reducing the proportion of kerosene produced. Between 1910 and 1919 this simple expedient doubled the amount of gasoline available; without it, an additional 80 million barrels of crude oil would have been needed to supply the demand for motor fuel in 1919. The resulting fuel was not very well handled by the carburettors of the time and it had an extremely bad tendency to knock (*see below*), but it could be improved somewhat by blending in some of the condensed volatile fractions ('natural' or 'casing-head' gasoline) that were not normally retained in the gasoline fraction. A thriving industry grew up before 1920 specializing in recovery of this material, and it supplied a significant fraction of the gasoline marketed.[12] Together, widening the cut and blending helped refiners to keep up with demand, but they offered no long-term solution to the supply problem; any crude oil contains only a finite amount of material that is naturally suitable for use as gasoline, petrol or *essence*.

As the lamp-oil refiners had done forty years before, gasoline suppliers turned to cracking to increase the yield of their product. In 1909, in the laboratories of the Standard Oil Company of Indiana, a group of university-trained chemists headed by William M. Burton began systematic studies on the thermal decomposition of high-boiling petroleum fractions that could be withdrawn from the market if desired.[13] After finding that petroleum vapours yielded mostly gaseous products and that the heavy residues from distillation were completely unmanageable, the group turned its attention to gas-oil, one of the higher-boiling fractions produced in the first refining stage. Heating this material under moderate pressure gave a mixture of liquid products, of which a significant fraction boiled in the gasoline range, and Burton's group then scaled up their 100-gallon experimental unit to full size. In spite of difficulties with existing equipment (for example, large pressure vessels could not be welded, but had to be riveted and leaked flammable petroleum at every joint until coke formation sealed the gaps), by 1913 Burton and his colleagues had put into operation a pressure-cracking unit that converted 23 per cent of its charge into gasoline. With some difficulty Burton persuaded his directors to spend $1 million to build sixty cracking stills. The production version was a horizontal cylindrical unit, 8 ft in diameter and 30 ft long, in which gas-oil was heated to 700° to 750°F under a pressure of 75 pounds per square inch; an 8,000-gallon charge could be processed every 48 hours. The product was a good motor fuel requiring little finishing treatment; it was marketed separately at first but later was blended with straight-run gasoline. Its success was immediate: cracking capacity had expanded tenfold by 1919 and tenfold again in the next three years.[14] The process was improved by other Standard workers and by 1920 Burton pressure stills were being operated semicontinuously at pressures up to 200 pounds per square inch.

Standard granted licences for the Burton process to fourteen other companies, and in seven years the royalties, together with Standard's own production, yielded the company a profit estimated at $95 million. The licensees earned some $60 million for themselves.[15] More important, the Burton process stimulated the development of better equipment and the investigation of alternative processes. Much effort was devoted to achieving the results of the Burton process, or to improving it in some detail, without flagrantly infringing Burton's patent. Before 1920 at least three economically competitive cracking processes had been developed, one of them by a man with the improbable but irresistible name of Carbon Petroleum Dubbs.[16]

The Problem of Knock

Early automobile engines went through many changes in mechanical design in the first two decades, and problems of carburation, valving and ignition were solved, or at least workable compromises were arrived at, without reference to any possible improvements in the fuel. The engines of the early twentieth century were comparatively low-speed, low-power machines having compression ratios averaging about 4.3:1,[17] and they worked well enough on the highly variable fuel that was available. But certain short-comings of these engines were well known. In particular, it was recognized that the thermal efficiency — and therefore the power per unit volume of displacement — of an internal-combustion engine depended upon its compression ratio, which is the ratio of cylinder volume at the bottom of the intake stroke to the volume at the top of the compression stroke.* Ideally the maximum thermal efficiency of an engine could be raised by one-third if the compression ratio could be increased from 4:1 to 7:1 and, while no real engine approached ideal thermal efficiency, significant gains in power and fuel economy could be realized by increasing this ratio. A 7:1 compression ratio was not impossible, although high-compression engines would have been far heavier; what limited the usable compression ratio was the behaviour of the available fuels.

Subjected to compression greater than about 5.5:1, straight-run gasolines (i.e. untreated distillates) had a bad tendency to 'knock'. This phenomenon, so-called because of the characteristic rattling noise associated with it, was not understood, but its effects were plain: loss of power, overheating, and damage to pistons and associated parts. Knocking was recognized as wasteful, damaging and something to be avoided — by keeping compression ratios low.

Not much was to be gained by increasing the power and fuel efficiency of automobile engines, considering the many other factors that affected the use of the automobile. But the airplane, emerging from the embryonic state as the 1914–18 war began, presented a different case. For aircraft engines a high power-to-weight ratio was essential — a requirement that grew more stringent as the war wore on; and improved defensive weapons created demands for increased power, speed and ceiling. And if the airplane was to have any future in civilian commerce, better fuel economy was mandatory to increase its endurance and payload capacity. Higher compression ratios were imperative, but they could not be realized using the fuel available around 1918.

Thus to the pressure for *more* fuel was added the pressure for *better* fuel. Clearly, refining practices had to change, but few people had any idea how it was to be done. Petroleum refining was historically an extractive industry, capable (within limits) of responding to increased demand but baffled by

---

*Strictly speaking, the expansion ratio is the determining factor. Some attempts were made to make expansion greater than compression, but the mechanical complexities were too high a price to pay for the small advantage gained.[18]

requirements for a different quality, which depended upon the nature of the raw material. In spite of wide variations in its properties, crude oil yielded much the same kinds of distillates regardless of its source and, therefore, a search for better motor fuel seemed unlikely to be fruitful. And notwithstanding the recognition of cracking as a chemical transformation, refiners viewed it merely as a means of increasing their output. Only later was it realized that cracked gasoline was better than straight-run distillate.

For its part, chemistry was not well prepared to help the refiners. The chemical entities that predominated in most crude oils were of a type (aliphatic) that had received less attention from academic chemists than had been given to coal-tar derivatives (aromatics); hence a comparatively small body of knowledge was available on which to base any contemplated chemical modification of petroleum. Burton and others like him could understand and intelligently control a process such as cracking, but chemical theory provided few guidelines for exploring beyond the frontier. Indeed, until refiners understood why some fuels were good and others were bad, chemists could not even know what to investigate.

INVESTIGATING KNOCK

All refining processes were operated so as to yield a product having the physical properties (boiling range and specific gravity) known to be desirable in a motor fuel. Refiners apparently applied no other tests of quality; the ultimate indication seems to have been acceptance by the motoring consumer. But by 1915 it was becoming increasingly evident, and increasingly intolerable, that virtually nothing was known about the combustion process, or the knocking phenomenon, or almost anything about the essential nature of a good motor fuel. After the war the Asiatic Petroleum Company financed a basic study of the fuel–engine relationship, to be conducted by the engineering consulting firm of Ricardo and Company, headed by Harry R. (later Sir Harry) Ricardo.

Ricardo, who had studied under Hopkinson at Cambridge, probably knew as much about internal-combustion engines as any man then alive, having worked for years to improve performance and fuel economy by refinements in engine design. His patent on a design for a cylinder head provided the royalties that sustained the consulting firm he established in 1917. As a result of his work Ricardo had come to realize that engine design and fuel properties were inextricably linked. The inadequacy of available information concerning fuels was made clear by his wartime experience designing engines for aircraft and tanks.[19] Without basic knowledge of fuel characteristics, research into engine design was hampered.

For the Asiatic Petroleum study, Ricardo assembled a team of scientists and engineers, including David R. Pye and Henry Tizard, whose expertise encompassed the entire range of questions that were likely to arise, from mechanical engineering to chemistry. Using an ingenious and thoroughly instrumented test engine and several samples of good and bad fuels, Ricardo's group systematically studied all the factors known to affect engine performance. Their results were embodied in a report that stood for twenty years as the definitive work on the subject. Some of their findings went against widely-held beliefs and clarified a number of poorly-understood points; in the language of Ricardo's report:

(1) It has been proved that the tendency of a fuel to detonate [an alternative term for knocking] is the one outstanding factor in determining its value for use in an internal combustion engine. Compared with this, all other considerations are of secondary importance.

...

(10) ... the performance of any combination of hydrocarbons as regards detonation ... is the mean performance of each of the components. The performance of any complex fuel such as petrol can therefore be predicted, once the nature and proportion of its components are determined, or conversely, a fuel can be prepared to give any required performance within the limits available.

(11) No increase in power or efficiency has been found or need be expected from the use of 'dopes' ... but certain substances, notably tetra-ethyl lead, when added in small quantities, tend to suppress detonation.

(12) The highest useful compression ratio for ... any petrol is governed by the relative proportions of aromatics, naphthenes, and paraffins it contains — the smaller the proportion of the latter the better....

(13) To judge the quality of a fuel by its specific gravity is entirely misleading....

...

(15) There is considerable evidence to indicate that in the case of most 'natural' petrols the more valuable constituents are those of which the boiling points lie between the range 80°C to 180°C. It is therefore quite as undesirable to restrict the final boiling point of a fuel to 150°C as it is to permit it to exceed 200°C. ....[20]

Besides evaluating hydrocarbon fuels, the group also conducted tests on the performance of alcohols, and Ricardo suggested in 1923 that ethyl alcohol, which was in some respects a superior fuel and which could be produced from renewable resources, was the long-term answer to the impending shortage of gasoline. But experience forced him to conclude that nothing would be done about it until the shortage actually came to pass.[21]

Ricardo's study was of little immediate use to refiners, who at the time had no idea how to take advantage of his findings. For example, he found that benzene, though its high specific gravity ruled it out of consideration as a motor fuel, was extremely resistant to knocking. But benzene was neither cheap nor plentiful, and its occurrence in crude oil was apparently fortuitous. Crudes from Sumatra and Borneo contained substantial amounts of benzene and its chemical relatives, but the high-gravity distillates were being burnt as waste at the refineries because they were thought to be useless.[22] And although the study had shown that paraffin hydrocarbons were the least desirable components of petroleum distillates, refining technology could not reduce the proportion of paraffins normally present in the gasoline fraction.

One practical result of the Asiatic Company's study was the establishment of a means of comparing the anti-knock qualities of different fuels. For this comparison Ricardo devised a 'toluene number' scale, assigning pure toluene (an excellent fuel) a value of 100 and pure heptane (a very poor fuel) a value of zero. In a test engine whose compression ratio could be varied while the engine was in operation, he burned mixtures of varying proportions of toluene and heptane to determine the highest compression ratio that did not produce knock, thus establishing a correlation between the highest usable compression ratio and the percentage of toluene in the test fuel. Any commercial fuel could then be assigned a 'toluene number' by similarly determining its highest usable compression ratio in the test engine. This was the forerunner of the 'octane number' scale, a lineal descendant of which is still in use. As a result of this work, Shell Petroleum adopted the practice of blending gasoline stocks to a constant toluene number.[23]

Among those who made immediate use of Ricardo's work was the team of Captain John Alcock and Lieutenant Arthur Whitten Brown, two RAF officers who were preparing to attempt a non-stop transatlantic flight. On the basis of Ricardo's advice, Shell Petroleum blended a supply of high-quality fuel especially for their flight.[24] Modification of the engines of their Vimy bomber to take advantage of this fuel blend extended the range and payload (and therefore the fuel capacity), and Alcock and Brown successfully flew from St John's, Newfoundland, to Ireland on 14–15 June 1919.

Almost simultaneously with Ricardo's study, an independent and fundamentally different approach to the knocking problem was being taken on the other side of the Atlantic. In 1916 the American engineer Charles F. Kettering had begun a search for a substance that could be added to motor fuel to suppress knock. After early work had shown that the idea had some merit, Kettering turned the project over to Thomas Midgley, jnr, in 1919. Guided sometimes by wrong hypotheses, proceeding sometimes by pure trial and error, Midgley found that several chemical compounds, when added in small quantities to gasoline, gave higher usable compression ratios and significant improvements in power and fuel economy. Finally one compound, tetraethyl lead, was found to have the optimum combination of properties. A serious drawback was its tendency to deposit lead in the cylinders, but ethylene bromide added along with the anti-knock compound converted the lead to lead bromide, which is sufficiently volatile at engine temperatures to be carried out with the exhaust. There followed a remarkable development project to manufacture and market the additive — remarkable in that nothing like tetraethyl lead (an unusual organometallic compound, strictly a laboratory material) had ever been made commercially, and bromine, a rare element required to make ethylene bromide, had never been produced in anything like the quantities required. The product was marketed as 'Ethyl fluid' and at first it was added to gasoline at the pump at the option of the customer. Later the additives were mixed with the fuel by the refiner and 'Ethyl' gasoline was supplied separately at a premium price.

Midgley's study can be said to have been less scientific, more cut-and-try than Ricardo's (although this is disputed), but it was based on a much more realistic appraisal of the immediate technological problem of reducing knock. Ricardo hoped to understand the combustion process and relate knocking to the chemical composition of the fuel, but he was primarily concerned with improving fuel economy and performance through changes in engine design and therefore needed merely to be able to separate effects due to the fuel from those due to the engine. Midgley and Kettering sought a simple, economical means of converting poor fuel into good fuel, seeing this as the best practical solution to the problem of increasing the supply of motor fuel. On this point, Midgley convincingly argued that the nature of petroleum limited what could be done by refining and chemical transformation.[25] He was, in the main, correct; sixty years of improvements in refining and chemical conversion have not weakened his argument, although much more can be done now than in 1922.

Tetraethyl lead was the first instance of the use of an additive to overcome a particular problem — a practice that would later be adopted extensively for many other purposes. The new anti-knock compound was widely adopted, especially by American refiners, in the motoring market. Addition of a few cubic centimetres of Ethyl fluid per gallon of gasoline could raise the octane rating by 5 to 10 numbers, thus converting much marginally unsatisfactory gasoline into marketable fuel. But helpful though it was in increasing the gasoline supply, tetraethyl lead was of limited effectiveness, both technically and economically. Users of aviation fuel were not especially enthusiastic about the additive; the possibility of increased engine wear from lead fouling made other methods more attractive. Specifications for aviation fuel for the Royal Air Force did not allow the use of tetraethyl lead until the 1930s.[26]

Fuel Quality and Engine Design

In spite of the availability of better fuels after the mid-1920s, the compression ratio of automobile engines did not rise dramatically. Price competition in the mass automobile market was keen; the pressure to keep costs down made design changes slow, and other improvements — such as the completely closed car — took precedence over increased power and fuel economy. Further, the American highway system, though improving, was not yet conducive to extensive long-distance motoring. There was no question that America had 'discovered' the automobile, but the demand for increased speed, power and flexibility — 'high performance' — was not yet a major influence on design. Thus the advantages to be gained from high-compression engines and better fuels were comparatively small.

With full realization of the importance of Midgley's and Ricardo's work came the adoption of a quantitative scale for the evaluation of fuel quality. Ricardo's 'toluene number' was superseded in 1927 by the 'octane number' scale, which used 'iso-octane' (a trivial name for the chemical compound 2,2,4-trimethylpentane) instead of toluene as the standard 'best' anti-knock fuel. Refiners and engine designers had, for the first time, an objective measure of fuel quality that could be used to evaluate the effect of changes in fuel composition or engine design and could systematically investigate the relation of anti-knock value to chemical structure of fuel components.

Changes in Refining Technology

Through the 1920s, petroleum-refining technology changed considerably. Refining and cracking capacity continued to expand. Continuous processing displaced batch operation as the normal mode of refinery operation and great improvements were made in equipment. The bubble-cap fractionating tower, capable of continuously and efficiently separating three or four grades of distillate, came into use in 1924.[27] Thermal cracking remained the principal method of increasing the gasoline supply. Processes were improved in detail but not fundamentally changed, and the industry seemed to be gathering strength for its next creative expansion. The most important change, coming as the decade drew to a close, was the institutionalization of basic research into all aspects of refining technology and chemical conversion by most of the major refiners — not only searching for processes that would even fractionally push up the yield or quality of gasoline but also seeking a better understanding of the chemistry of petroleum hydrocarbons.

In addition to the ordinary economic pressure to squeeze the last drop of marketable product out of each barrel of crude, a pressure to conserve crude oil reserves became substantial during the 1920s. The conviction was growing that a shortage of crude oil was not far off,[28] which meant that it was imperative to maximize the amount of gasoline obtained from each barrel. This attitude was expressed by William Burton in 1922 on the occasion of accepting the Perkin Medal from the American Chemical Society. He noted that whereas in 1910 the United States had consumed approximately 700 million gallons of gasoline, in 1920 production amounted to 4,600 million gallons — almost a sevenfold increase, although in the same period domestic crude oil production had not even doubled. 'The American people,' Burton said, 'are notoriously wasteful in the use of natural resources with which they are so richly endowed. It is hoped that the [cracking process] will be considered a slight contribution toward the curtailment of such waste.' Thermal cracking, which accounted for nearly one-sixth of the gasoline production of the United States and Canada, 'conserv[ed] for future consumption an amount of crude oil nearly equal to one hundred million barrels per year'.[29] Subsequent discoveries,* both in the United States and abroad, allayed the fears of impending shortage (for some fifty years, at any rate), but the conservationist attitude was useful in curbing waste and promoting the utilization of the by-products from cracking.

Progress After 1930

The 1930s saw the commercialization of the most important advance in refining technology in the century: catalytic cracking.[30] Catalysis — the use of an otherwise inert substance to increase the rate of a chemical reaction — was well known and applied to commercial processes (for example, hydrogenation of vegetable oils), but little theory was available to guide the search for a catalyst to promote a specific reaction. Eugene J. Houdry, who experimented with the catalytic hydrogenation of lignite in 1920–5, discovered in 1927 that heating crude oil with a silica-alumina catalyst (a natural clay-like mineral) produced a volatile liquid product that was an excellent motor fuel (octane number up to 91 without further treatment). Commercialization of the process proved difficult, however. In its original form Houdry's process could not be operated continuously; during cracking, tar and coke coated the catalyst and rendered it inactive, and reactors had to be taken off stream to burn off the carbonaceous deposits. Batch operation was thus required, reactors being alternately charged and regenerated. Only with several reactors could a plant operate continuously and then well below its rated capacity. Initially, therefore, catalytic cracking could not match the yield or cost of thermal cracking processes. Against these drawbacks stood the high quality of the products: the gasoline was better than the regular grade of leaded gasoline, even without tetraethyl lead, and the heavier by-product was a fuel oil superior to that obtained by thermal cracking. Furthermore, the heat produced during regeneration of the catalyst could be captured and used, making the process almost independent of outside power.[31]

By 1936, developmental difficulties had been overcome sufficiently for Socony-Vacuum to put Houdry units into production; the following year the Sun Oil Company did likewise. In two years the Houdry process had been improved to the point that it could boast a price advantage of $0.07 per barrel over thermally-cracked gasoline, and other companies applied for licences. Standard of New Jersey, however, failed to come to terms with Houdry and instead took the lead in forming a combine to conduct research into catalytic cracking. The combine spent $15 million in three years, devising a continuous process in which the catalyst was moved from reactor to regenerator and back. In the course of this work it was discovered that finely-divided catalyst particles could be suspended in a moving stream of gas to produce a phase that behaved much like a liquid. This led to new

*The East Texas field, discovered just eight years after Burton spoke, produced 4,000 million barrels of crude oil in the next forty years, an average of 100 million barrels per year.

methods of transferring large quantities of solid from reactor to regenerator, separating the solids from the gas stream and returning them to the reactor.[32]

Despite the depression of 1930–8, demand for gasoline in the United States remained high. Average personal income declined by 25 per cent before rising again, but gasoline consumption declined during only two years in that period and then by only about 5 per cent; automobile registrations declined in roughly the same proportion.[33] An extensive programme of road improvements trebled the nation's mileage of paved roads between 1929 and 1941. If the automobile was the mainstay of petroleum refining, aviation provided a stimulus for change. Both civil and military aviation advanced steadily during the 1930s, aiming towards long-range sustained flight as well as high performance.

The anti-knock quality of gasoline rose during the 1930s roughly in parallel with an increase in engine compression ratios. In 1931 the average compression ratio for American cars was 5.23:1; in 1935, 5.98:1; and in 1939, 6.32:1. Average octane ratings for gasoline in those same years were 63 to 75, 72 to 78, and 74.5 to 83.[34] Whatever these 'averages' may mean, they show that the motor fuel marketed during this period was adequate for the engines of the time, but only just.*

Petroleum refining — which by this time should more accurately be termed gasoline production — drew more and more heavily upon chemical conversion of the less valuable crude oil fractions into the more valuable motor fuels. The understanding of the chemical characteristics of high-quality fuels provided the plan, and the demonstrated power of catalysis the tools, for this shift of emphasis. Before 1930, cracking had already supplanted distillation as the main source of motor fuel. As one consequence, large and steady supplies of gaseous by-products were available to refiners. In earlier days these by-product hydrocarbon gases had been used as refinery fuel or simply burnt as waste; by the mid-1930s processes to convert them to gasoline components were well along in development. New catalytic synthetic processes, fabricating large molecules out of small ones, were capable of turning cracking by-products into intermediates requiring only one additional step to convert them into iso-octane, the standard of maximum anti-knock quality. In 1934, Shell Oil Company delivered a 1,000-gallon lot of iso-octane to the US Army Air Corps for testing — a milestone in fuel technology, which theretofore had dealt chiefly with mixtures, not with essentially pure chemical compounds. It was a portent of the monumental effort that would be mounted eight years later.[37]

---

*Data from a mechanic's handbook[35] show that in 1935 the compression ratios of the three most popular American cars ranged from 5.6:1 to 6.7:1, establishing a requirement of 65 to 87 for the octane rating of their fuel.[36] For 1940 the corresponding figures were 6.15:1 to 6.7:1 and 80 to 87 octane. It appears — if the octane ratings given above are accurate — that the owners of cars with high-compression engines could not get maximum performance from their vehicles using the premium grade of fuel available; engines with lower compression ratios, however, should have performed well even on the lower grade.

The groundwork for this accomplishment had been laid starting in the late 1920s, when refiners began to give significant support to both pure and applied research in petroleum chemistry and technology. The experience of Shell may be taken as typical. The company established an independent research and development branch in 1928, not only to improve refining technology and promote the utilization of refinery by-products but also to acquire fundamental data concerning cracking and other catalytic processes and to develop a basic science of petroleum chemistry.[38] In enlisting the support of basic science, the petroleum industry was following the precedent set by the German dye industry nearly a century before, and the consequences were equally far-reaching.

How soon the fruits of this work would have reached the average motorist can only be conjectured. The new processes required order-of-magnitude improvements in distillation and process control, and in normal times might have taken years to reach commercial production. The outbreak of war in 1939 changed all that, however. Hitler's war was far more demanding of petroleum refiners than the Kaiser's had been; it was from the outset a motorized war, one in which the greatest resources in petroleum and mechanical technology would determine the outcome. In particular, the demands of the air war evoked additional technological ingenuity as it became common to use fuel with an octane rating of 100 — even higher towards the war's end. With generous government assistance under the pressures of war, America's petroleum refiners quickly developed their embryonic capability to produce vast quantities of aviation gasoline, using methods undreamed of twenty years earlier. The capability thus developed would be the industry's mainstay in the postwar motoring era.

The wartime experience completed a fundamental transformation of the petroleum refining industry. The physical separation of crude oil into a few ill-defined fractions came to represent only the starting point for refining. Refining had become a branch of the chemical industry, capable of transforming the complex mixtures that constitute petroleum into high-quality fuel components by means of highly-specific chemical reactions. More important, through its solid commitment to chemical research, the industry acquired a flexibility and versatility that would enable it to respond to quite different challenges in the postwar decades.

Notes

1. T. K. Derry and Trevor L. Williams, *A Short History of Technology*, London, 1960, pp. 516–23. James A. Ruffner, 'Two Problems in Fuel Technology' in *History of Technology 1978*, pp. 125–35.

2. Harold F. Williamson, Ralph L. Andreano, Arnold R. Daum and Gilbert C. Klose, *The American Petroleum Industry*, Evanston, Ill., 1963, Vol. II, pp. 204–5.

3. Harold F. Williamson and Arnold R. Daum, *The American Petroleum Industry*, Evanston, Ill., 1959, Vol. I, pp. 202–31, 263–73.

4. Williamson and Daum, as note 3, pp. 53, 205–9, 218–21.

5. Williamson and Daum, as note 3, p. 678.

6. Sir Harry Ricardo, *Memories and Machines*, London, 1968, p. 60.

7. Williamson *et al.*, as note 2, pp. 113–14.

8. A.W. Nash and D.A. Howes, *The Principles of Motor Fuel Preparation and Application*, London, 1935, Vol. II, p. 492.

9. Williamson *et al.*, as note 2, p. 194.

10. Williamson *et al.*, as note 2, p. 190.

11. Williamson *et al.*, as note 2, p. 16.

12. Williamson *et al.*, as note 2, p. 133.

13. Williamson *et al.*, as note 2, pp. 136–62.

14. William M. Burton, 'Address of Acceptance [of the Perkin Medal]' in *J. Ind. Eng. Chem.*, 14, 1922, pp. 162–3.

15. Williamson and Daum, as note 3, pp. 147–50.

16. Williamson and Daum, as note 3, pp. 150–62.

17. Sir Dugald Clerk and G.A. Burls, *The Gas, Petrol, and Oil Engine*, London, 1913, Vol. II, Chapter VII.

18. D.R. Pye, *The Internal Combustion Engine*, London, 1937, Vol. I, pp. 21–2.

19. Ricardo, as note 6, pp. 182–97, 231–2.

20. H.R. Ricardo, 'The Influence of Various Fuels on Performance of Internal Combustion Engines' in the Report of the Empire Fuels Committee, published as Part I of Volume SVIII of *Proceedings of the Institute of Automotive Engineers*, London, 1924, pp. 51–155.

21. H.R. Ricardo, *The Internal Combustion Engine*, London, 1923, Vol. II, p. 3. Certain commercial gasolines have contained a proportion of alcohol, which is also employed in special fuels.

22. Ricardo, as note 6, p. 188.

23. Ricardo, as note 20, p. 90.

24. Ricardo, as note 6, pp. 207–8.

25. Midgley, T., jnr., *J. Ind. Eng. Chem.*, 14, 1922, p. 849.

26. Nash and Howes, as note 8, pp. 206–16.

27. Williamson *et al.*, as note 2, pp. 423–30.

28. Ricardo, as note 21.

29. Burton, as note 14.

30. Williamson *et al.*, as note 2, pp. 612–26.

31. Williamson *et al.*, as note 2, pp. 612–26.

32. E.V. Murphree, C.L. Brown, H.G.M. Fischer, E.J. Gohr and W.J. Sweeney, 'Fluid Catalyst Process' in *J. Ind. Eng. Chem.*, 35, 1943, pp. 768–73.

33. Williamson *et al.*, as note 2, p. 654–6.

34. Williamson *et al.*, as note 2, p. 607; Nash and Howes, as note 8, pp. 206–16.

35. Harold F. Blanchard, ed., *Motor's Auto Repair Manual*, 16th ed., New York, 1963.

36. Pye, as note 18, p. 251.

37. Kendall Beaton, *Enterprise in Oil: A History of Shell in the United States*, New York, 1957, p. 535.

38. Beaton, as note 37, pp. 517–53.

Wood Since the Industrial Revolution: a Strategic Retreat?

F. T. EVANS

We usually accept the Industrial Revolution at its own self-valuation as bringing the swift, wholesale replacement of wood by iron. Journalists, poets and propagandists presented such a picture of the age. Perhaps influenced by this, historians have mostly discussed wood in terms of supply and demand. Fixing their eyes too firmly on the development of metals, they have been tempted to ignore wood's properties and uses. Economic historians often see wood merely as the material which became scarce and so led to the growth of the coal and iron industries during the Industrial Revolution. Deane's 'First Industrial Revolution', for instance, names the shortage of wood in 1750 as the main bottleneck in the British economy, mentions some of its uses and then scathingly describes it as 'unsatisfactory as a construction material because it was clumsy, rapidly worn out by weather or friction and easily burnt so that it had a short life on the average and was not very adaptable when used for the working parts of machinery. Its shortage restricted the output of industries which depended on it for fuel, of which the most important was the iron industry.'[1] This is a standard economic history view: yet in the 1960s Americans used 2,400 lb of wood annually per head and only 1,100 lb of steel. The world uses 2,500,000,000 cubic metres of wood each year. Much of it is burnt; but 56 per cent, say 900,000,000 tons, is used as timber or converted into other material. Since the world produced 650 million tons of steel in 1970, the consumption of wood is greater by nearly half.[2] It is worth wondering what happened to a material which has been written off as obsolete in the eighteenth century and yet is plainly the most widely-used material today.

This article will suggest that the quantitative approach can only partly explain the changing relationship between wood and iron. More understanding of the properties and uses of particular species of wood is also needed. Closer attention should also be paid to wood in the different branches of engineering. Shipbuilding, factories, civil engineering and aviation each had individual technical conditions to satisfy. It may be that a technical analysis can provide a different perspective from the quantitative approach based on supply and demand.

Wood as a Fuel

It is true that wood declined relatively as a fuel and that new forms of energy — coal, oil and electricity — have grown; though in rural France one still sees large woodstacks by the house and wood-burning seems to be entering a new vogue in Britain. The degree to which scarcity was responsible for the change has been much discussed, but plainly wood was dearer in large towns than in remote rural areas. Benjamin Franklin was speaking of the same thing even in the America of 1745. 'Wood, our common fuel, which within these hundred years might be had at every man's door, must now be fetched near one hundred miles to some towns, and makes a very considerable article in the expence of families.'[3] Professor Flinn has shown that the iron industry up to 1750 was not so constricted by shortage of wood fuel as has been often supposed.[4] Nevertheless, it is inconceivable that British forests could have supported the vast increase in iron production which took place around 1800.

The special properties of wood as a fuel are less frequently explored. Perhaps the twentieth-century mind is so accustomed to using the general concept of energy that it is worth emphasizing the individuality of eighteenth-century fuel applications. Wood fuel had unique virtues. It made little ash; burning a thousand pounds of pine, oak or willow leaves less than five pounds of ash; and many woods are free from impurities like phosphorus and sulphur.[5] Beech is particularly clean chemically and was used by glass blowers when welding on the handles. (Mineral coal lets sulphur combine with lead in the glass and turns it black.) Willow and alder made excellent charcoal for gunpowder and for this reason powder mills often occupied the swampy country favoured by those trees.[6] An odder use for wood fuel is still to be seen in rolling armour plate. Masses of hazel twigs are thrown on to the red hot metal as it passes under the rolls, and the twigs explode, blowing off the oxide scale. Nor should we forget the wood-smoke which preserves bacon, fish and cheese. Fruit-tree timbers, and mast-bearing trees like oak and beech, give the best flavour. In the Second World War, a whole consignment of bacon was spoilt by smoking it with cedar wood.

On the other hand, wood is a bulky fuel to store. Even dense timbers with an inflammable resin content take up far more space than the coal of an equivalent heat value.[7] The friability of wood charcoal made it difficult to transport; it crushed to powder if there was too much weight on it. Consequently blast furnaces could grow much higher when coke took over as their fuel. All solid fuels are at a disadvantage compared with gas and liquid fuels which can be pumped. The motor car would not be so popular if it needed a stoker, though during the war many vehicles in Nazi-occupied Europe were fitted with generators producing carbon monoxide gas from wood. In general, wood is a particularly poor fuel for transport because it needs so much storage space. River steamers which can pick up frequent supplies of cordwood were viable but a transatlantic steamer was a quite different matter. The overall trend in energy use has been towards higher temperatures, compactness and flexibility: the sequence has been wood, coal, oil, nuclear fuel — and it is interesting to speculate on the future of the progression.

The Supply of Wood

As an engineering material, wood was everywhere in the 1700s. Metals and other materials were used, of course, but wood was almost universal. In 1720 Britain produced 26,000 tons of cast iron—only 9 pounds per head of the population. Boxes, plates, floors, roofs, walls, fences, gates, carts, furniture, forge hammers, all kinds of machines, looms and ships were made of wood. Apart from the grinding stones and a few pounds of iron, a whole water mill or windmill could be built of timber, including the fastenings. Ships and other artefacts were held together by trenails, or dowels, and this was not an unsatisfactory way—if a structure is likely to flex, and wooden carts and ships certainly do that, then hard iron nails will wear their holes bigger but dowels will not.[8] Of course this put great demands on Britain's woodlands. David Mushet in 1824 reckoned that a charcoal furnace would use 30,000 sacks of charcoal per year—the produce of 120 acres of woodland; since this would take twenty years to replace, it meant 2,400 acres of wood to keep the furnace running.[9]

Ship-building also laid heavy demands on supplies. A seventy-four gun ship took 1,236 tons of oak to build. Such an exceptional tree as one felled in 1791 in Monmouthshire might supply 1,195 cubic feet, or 23 tons, of usable timber; but in the 1850s a tree often gave only 50 cubic feet. At forty trees to the acre, forty acres were needed to provide the timber for one third-rate. If the ship lasted twenty years and the oak trees needed a century to grow, then each vessel was tying up 200 acres of woodland. The British Navy in 1813 possessed 259 ships of the line, and 320 vessels as big or bigger than frigates. We could be speaking, therefore, of 120,000 acres of forest to maintain the navy's larger vessels alone—an area of less than ten miles by twenty. Between 1760 and 1788, nine-tenths of the timber used by the dockyards was English grown—amounting to 37,563 loads of 50 cubic feet per annum.[10] All this supports Michael Flinn's view that: 'So far from there being a timber famine, it is abundantly clear that the supply of both timber and cordwood during the two centuries after 1550 was enormously increased with surprisingly little real increase in prices.'[11] If British forests were meeting the demand for timber, perhaps the real basis for anxiety was that they were not being replanted.

The seventeenth century witnessed the felling of timber of a quality we have never seen again. John Evelyn described its passing. 'In the Hall Park, neer unto Rivelin, stood an Oak which had eighteen yards without bough or, knot; and carried a *yard* and *six inches* square at the same height.' 'In the upper end of Rivelin stood a *Tree*, call'd the Lords-Oak, of twelve yards about . . .' In Sheffield Park an oak trunk was lying: '*Sam Staniforth a Keeper*, and *Ed Morphy*, both on horseback, could not see over the *Tree* one anothers hat-crowns.' In Worksop Park stood a tree which measured 180 ft from tip of bough to tip of bough, so it shaded 2,827 square yards 'which is above half an acre of ground: and the assigning three square yards for an horse, there may 942 be well said to stand in this compass'. The trees like this have gone, and much of our modern conifer production is fit only for chipboard:

'For now Rivelin itself is totally destitute of that issue she once might have gloried in of *Oaks*.'[12]

After Evelyn's time, the story of Britain's home-grown timber remained an unhappy one of neglect. Some landowners introduced useful new species like larch; others planted acorns for the navy.[13] But the overall impression is that the home timber trade atrophied because of cheap easy imports. Native oak, larch, chestnut, elm and lime were available 'but it is difficult to persuade tradesmen to work them. Four principal objections are urged by them against the use or working of these woods: 1st. The expense of sawing. 2nd. The difficulty of working. 3rd. The inferior look of British wood in inside finishing; and 4th. The greater labour and expense.'[14] These complaints in 1832 by the King's Forester for Scotland are echoed by a Chief Forestry Officer in 1910: 'it is probable that sufficient timber could be grown in existing woodlands to supply the needs of agricultural districts, for it is a well known fact that large quantities of foreign timber are imported into them more by reason of its well seasoned and prepared condition, than on account of the actual scarcity of the home grown article.'[15] The Forestry Commission's census of 1924 showed that less than half of Britain's three million acres of woodland was even reasonably productive, while 27 per cent was producing nothing at all. In 1939 the home timber merchant was still having to deal with mixed quantities, low grades and varying supplies, in contrast to the low-price, reliable quality and continuity of foreign timber supplies.[16] This neglect of home timber would scarcely seem rational conduct in a nation that was supposed to be undergoing a wood famine, but it is evident that imported timber met Britain's needs.

Britain had long been a substantial importer of wood. From the thirteenth century, words like 'waynescote' and 'estrich boards' (from Eastreich) testify to a consumption of Baltic woods, and it was said that the Norwegian timber merchants warmed themselves comfortably by the Great Fire of London in 1666 — an allusion to the great quantities of fir imported for reconstruction.[17] British naval power could guarantee Baltic supplies even in wartime, and after 1600 new timbers came increasingly from the Americas, Africa, India and South-East Asia. The price of Quebec oak fell from £6 to £4 10s a ton in 1851 because there was so little demand — and this, very significantly, was just before the Royal Navy changed from wooden to iron ships.[18] Fine softwoods, mahoganies and teaks flowed into the ports as new forests were opened to British trade. 'There are forests of jarrah in Western Australia of more than four miles in depth, and which are known to extend for a length of 150 miles. Here, then, is timber enough to maintain our navy for a hundred years to come. . . .'[19] By 1900 Britain was importing 10,000,000 tons of wood annually. There was no crippling shortage of wood to explain the increased use of iron in the late eighteenth and nineteenth or twentieth centuries.

The Properties of Wood

We have been talking about quantities, but there are limits to how far one can discuss wood in either quantitative or general terms. Timbers differ radically in their character and uses, and generalizations about the internal structure of wood can only go a certain way towards explaining its properties. It is important, of course, to understand that both softwoods and hardwoods are composed of cellulose tubes, with some differences between the two families, and that these strong tubes are held together laterally in a weaker matrix. Hence wood is often weak across the grain, remarkably strong in tension along the grain, but rather weaker in compression because the tubes can buckle. Here at once is the reason why wooden planks nearly always have members running across them, such as the massive framing of a ship of the line or the joists running beneath floorboards. The internal structure of wood gives it some similar properties to those of the modern bonded-fibre materials. Wood is very resistant to the crack propagation and brittle fractures which plague some modern materials. In this respect, it curiously resembles wrought iron, whose fibrous nature is clearly revealed when the surface rusts.[20]

Broadly speaking, the heavier the wood, the stronger it is. Balsawood has a density of only 6.5 lb per cubic foot — one-tenth that of water; whereas lignum vitae at the other extreme has a density of 75.5 lb per cubic foot and, like ebony and holm oak, simply sinks in water. Yet both lignum and balsa are strong in relation to their density and, weight for weight, wood is as strong as most steels.[21] We are, indeed, dealing with a very impressive material, but the full quality of wood only appears when we look at the astonishing variety of special characteristics and uses which belong to the individual species. In a cart wheel, for instance, the central stock was elm because it was hard and its curly grain stopped it splitting when the spokes were driven in. Windsor chair seats should be elm for the same reason, and so were the great keels of Nelson's ships which had to withstand the driving of 6-foot long bolts. Furthermore, elm did not rot under water and its cross grain resisted abrasion. Returning to the cart wheel, its spokes would be oak, the English hardwood which splits easily with a wedge down the grain. There should be no danger of spokes sawn across the grain failing under load. The rim of the wheel was usually ash, an elastic timber that withstands shocks and does not shatter.[22] Tool handles, carriage frames, even early car chassis and parts of aircraft fuselages liable to heavy blows were made of ash. The list of timber uses is long. Appleton's *Dictionary of Mechanics* gave no fewer than 133 timbers with their special engineering uses, and even this was not exhaustive.[23]

Walnut made gun butts. It was curly in the grain and tough to withstand the recoil; it did not warp or crack from shrinkage; and its sweet oils did not corrode the barrel. By contrast, the tannin in oak does corrode steel to form an unsightly black stain (though useful for ink making!). That is why brass screws are best with oak which is subject to damp. Again, what substitute is there for pencil cedar? It grooves easily and takes a fine paint finish; it can be cut obliquely to the grain with a blunt pen-knife; and it tastes nice.[24]

Cricket bats are blue willow, *Salix alba caerulea*: a very resilient wood whose thick-walled cells hold air which acts as a spring; it makes good artificial legs too. Hornbeam is almost a forgotten wood, yet it has few equals for toughness and wear-resistance. The great gear wheels of ancient water-powered machines had hornbeam teeth; if there was no hornbeam available, then crabapple served, or oak was used at a pinch.[25] Pear trees gave yet another timber with special qualities — not strength this time, but freedom from grain. It carved well in all directions and so was ideal for iron and brass founders' casting models and for woodblock printing. Lime is also a wood that carves well — it was Grinling Gibbons' favourite.[26] Dogwood was another of the tough timbers: it was chosen for weavers' shuttles, for delicate picks used by watch makers and also for meat skewers because it does not taint the meat.

The list seems endless. Alder works easily and is strong when wet so it used to make waterpipes and now makes clogs and broom-handles. Norway spruce — *Abies excelsa* — gave masts and house timbers; but in Lapland they boiled the roots to make string and in Norway the sweet inner bark was added to flour. Another conifer, the 'stone pine' of Central Europe, carved well and was sought after for wardrobes because, according to Tomlinson, it was remarkable for its 'fragrance, which it retains for centuries, much to the annoyance of bugs and moths, pestilent creatures which have an unconquerable antipathy to its neighbourhood'.[27]

Timbers have their drawbacks too. Ash, so strong under shock, will creep under sustained loads so is not good in structures; it is also very prone to rot in wet conditions. The sweetness of woods like beech and sycamore (which can be tapped for its sugary sap) makes them ready prey to insects. When there is a wood which insects dislike, like greenheart or teak, the workman must be careful that the wood does not harm human beings or perhaps their tools with noxious gums or hard silica. All this shows how difficult it is to discuss wood fully or sensibly in simple quantitative terms. Certainly it can be measured in terms of cost and volume, or tensile and compressive strengths, but we should not be misled by this into the modern functional heresy of forgetting that our quantitative analyses are not the whole of reality.

Many of these special uses of different woods have continued: ash or hickory tool handles; lignum vitae marine propeller-shaft bearings; cedar roof shingles. These are minor applications. We must ask about the major uses of wood — how quickly, and in what ways, did metal supplant wood? Was there a hasty search for substitutes, even inferior ones, caused by the 'shortage' of timber? The possible field of enquiry is too wide to tackle in full, so bridge building, ship building, mechanical engineering and aircraft construction will be taken as examples. This is a fair selection since in agriculture, house building or furniture making, wood has by no means disappeared. By taking major examples we can test the generalizations often made about the unsatisfactory nature, scarcity and consequent replacement of wood.

Wood in Bridges

Histories of bridge construction pay a great deal of attention to the development of iron bridges, beginning with that first cast-iron arch at Coalbrookdale in 1779. Telford and Robert Stephenson at Menai, Brunel at Clifton and Saltash, were setting a trend that leads with little interruption to our modern box girders and great suspension bridges. They were creative artists who have proved to be in the mainstream of engineering design; yet to leave the judgement at that point is to see the past too much in the light of the present. It is a 'whig interpretation' where the victors in a revolution become the judges of their vanquished opponents. The Coalbrookdale cast-iron bridge was only slowly imitated and it was nearly twenty years before others were built. The greatest span — for 600 ft across the Thames, proposed by Telford — was not built because engineers at the time could not decide whether it would be safe. Cast iron turned out to be a treacherous material for railway bridges. Robert Stephenson's cast-iron girders over the Dee collapsed and the subsequent inquiry found heavily against the material. I. K. Brunel disliked cast iron: 'Cast iron bridges are always giving trouble ... I never use cast iron myself if I can help it but in some cases it is necessary, and to meet these I have had girders cast of a particular mixture of iron. The number I have is few because as I have before said, I dislike them.'[28] Many of Brunel's railway viaducts were timber — thirty-four of them between Truro and Plymouth alone. Even his great Saltash railway bridge was designed originally as a 250 ft wooden span flanked by six 100 ft spans also in wood.

Wooden bridges may have been a short-term choice on account of their vulnerability to rot and fire, but they had their advantages too. They were very quick to build. An American viaduct over the Schuylkill was 1,018 ft long but took only three months in 1834 to complete, from the delivery of the first timber to waggons passing over it.[29] Timber bridges were successful over very long spans. The Schaffhausen bridge of Ulrich Grubenmann was in two arches of 172 and 193 ft span; C. F. von Wiebeking built a 206 ft span at Bamberg; and another over the Limmat at Wettingen was said to be 390 ft in one span.[30] Timber was an attractive proposition for spans like these if compared with the cost of centring for a stone arch or the erection of intermediate piers to reduce the span. In the mid-nineteenth century, timber preservation methods were still uncertain, but bridges could last well. Some of the Brunel bridges lasted into the 1930s and the magnificent satinwood arch of 205 ft span over the Mahawweliganga in Ceylon stood from 1833 until its replacement in 1905.[31] After 1800, civil engineers began to overcome the difficulty, fundamental to all large wooden structures, that they have to be jointed together strongly from smaller sections. One successful solution to the problem was the laminated arch, built up from thinner planks, bent and then fixed together with bolts or trenails. Von Wiebeking's bridges were like this and so were the riding school roofs built by A. R. Emy in France. Emy was confident that his laminated wooden arches could span 100 m.[32] More than thirty bridges of this kind were built for British railways between 1839 and 1850. These arches had spans of up to 150 ft, and they proved economical and durable.[33]

We are accustomed to think, like Nikolaus Pevsner, that what made the Great Exhibition building of 1851 'the outstanding example of mid-nineteenth century architecture was rather its enormous size . . . the absence of any other materials, and an ingenious system of prefabrication for the iron and glass parts'.[34] Yet, in fact, Paxton's 72-ft span transept arches, the longest in the building, were laminated out of Memel fir. The 205 miles of wooden sash bar and 34 miles of wooden guttering also played essential structural roles in the Crystal Palace.[35] Is it not possible that we have been taken in by the propaganda of the Industrial Revolution? Men like the ironfounder John Wilkinson and Erasmus Darwin proclaimed the new age of steam and iron and we have taken them at their face value, helped on our way by the belief that timber was in short supply.

It is true, of course, that iron and steel came to dominate in major structures, and that the threat of fire and rot, and the problems of working in wood, contributed to this. An equally important reason was the new structural forms which were developed for wrought iron, a milder and more reliable iron than cast, and stronger under tension and shock. At first it was only used in tension — as chains or bars — in suspension bridges. But Robert Stephenson's Britannia Bridge, with 460-ft long tubes, created structural forms which made wrought iron a stiff material and let it be used under compressive loads.[36] Brunel managed the same thing with his 'bowstring' arches at Windsor, Chepstow and Tamar. This ultimate defeat by wrought iron cannot conceal the fact that timber had successfully maintained its position against cast iron and masonry well into the Industrial Revolution. Indeed, new adhesives and fixings have renewed the prospects of wood as a structural material while not only cast, but wrought iron too, have retired into the shadows.

The Mechanical Engineer

The mechanical engineer presents a quite different picture from the civil; one is tempted to say that he came into being with the new age of iron. Whereas the civil engineer, as bridge builder in stone or wood or as water specialist, had roots in the pre-industrial past, the mechanical engineer was a newcomer, a creation of the nineteenth century. From Henry Maudslay and his pupils onwards, the mechanical engineer dealt in precision, rigidity and concentrated power.[37] Wood, swelling and shrinking with the humidity of the air, did not keep to the precise thousandths or even ten-thousandths of an inch which became the standard with Maudslay, Clement and Whitworth soon after 1800. The steam engine brought vibration, high pressures, concentrated power and high rotational speeds. To meet these new conditions, engineers had to make iron frameworks and shafting, and these replaced the wooden structures hitherto adequate for bulky, slow water-wheels and low-pressure beam engines. The old power technology had combined the skills of the mason and carpenter, who built the wooden wheel or engine beam into a masonry structure, with the mechanism held linked by a wooden framework. The overshot wheel, turning only four or five times per minute, gave out its power through thick, slow-turning wooden axles. As Professor Gordon points out, nature does not know rotation.[38] Bones and wooden beams stand bending and compression — but they fail in torsion. No, the new shafts and fast-turning axles had to be wrought iron. The new machine tools needed iron's rigidity to attain precision and powerful feeds, and so did the artefacts of precision. After all, wood would acquire little advantage from being very stiff in the process of evolution. Trees, very sensibly, absorb the energy of winds and shocks by deformation. Consequently there was little place for wood in the accurately-aligned mechanisms of typewriters, sewing machines or revolvers. The standards, respectability and identity of the mechanical engineer lay, from the beginning, with metal and he did not learn to design in wood.

We still hear echoes of the transition from wood, wind and water to steam and iron in the difference between millwrights and mechanical engineers. Millwrights are still noted for their ingenuity and workmanship in old industrial parts of Britain. They do not fit the modern pattern of professional qualifications and examinations; theirs is more a craft based on skill and experience. They work with equal ease on stone, metal and wood. Here, once again, we come to the iron and steam propaganda of the Industrial Revolution. Many wooden waterwheels and forging hammers went on working in Sheffield until well into the twentieth century. The eighteenth-century scythe forge at Abbeydale was still at work in the 1930s. Have we too easily accepted 'Iron Mad' Wilkinson's vision of an iron civilization, with his iron coffin, iron boat, iron pipes, and dreams of iron houses and ships? When was wood ever news? It had been there all the time, even if there were few references to it in the weekly *Mechanics Magazine*. After all, the methods of woodworking were very well known so it could be taken for granted.

Yet even for the new mechanical engineer, wood did play one important role. Many of the new machine tools, like the naval block-making equipment at Portsmouth and the American copying lathes for gun butts, were designed for working wood. The new production machines replaced the handwork of carpenters and joiners in the making of furniture, carriage wheels or pre-fabricated parts of buildings.[39] In doing so, perhaps the machines enforced a simplified view of wood as a passive material, limiting its possibilities to those of the machines which fashioned it.

This account of the mechanical engineers' attitude to wood may seem exaggerated, but some evidence suggests that there was a conscious jump from traditional ways. General Sir Samuel Bentham was a noted engineer and inventor of his day, though his brother Jeremy is now better known. Jeremy Bentham was the chief founder of the Utilitarian philosophy of politics, a rejection of tradition, superstition and precedent; he sought to make legislation and government a scientific process based on the simple principle of 'the greatest good of the greatest number' and to sweep away what he saw as all kinds of historical nonsense. Samuel Bentham seems to have been equally radical in his approach to machines. It is still not certain how much he contributed to the Portsmouth block-making machinery with which we chiefly associate the names of Henry Maudslay and Marc Isambard Brunel, but Bentham had already invented a considerable range of woodworking machinery before Brunel came on the scene in 1802. These machines included circular saws, planing machines, shapers and mortisers, and they represented a radical breakaway from the traditional hand-tool approach. 'By these patents, it will be seen that the several operations which have place in the working materials of various kinds were *classed* according to the nature of the *operations themselves*, instead of being left to the customary artificial and partial arrangements according to particular trades and handicrafts ... By this scientific classification, joined to the description of machines and engines, these patents indicate the mode by which nearly all the operations in working wood have been subsequently performed.'[40] Here we find a breach with the woodworking tradition. The new machines were not made to perpetuate the old trades of wheelwright, carpenter or cabinet maker. They were, instead, based on a general, abstract analysis of wood-shaping. One might go so far as to say that they were a mechanical analogy of his brother Jeremy's general, abstract analysis of legislation. Indeed, the two Benthams intended that the machinery should be used in Jeremy's proposed Panopticon, a sort of factory prison where the convicts would be usefully employed while being converted to the ways of society (as Jeremy saw them).

Wooden Ships

When we turn to the transition from wood to iron in naval shipbuilding, we come to a matter of great national concern where any proposed changes were hotly debated. It would be impossible to overestimate the importance of Britain's wooden navy as a force in her world strategy, as a factor in trade expansion or as a deeply emotional element in her national consciousness.[41] The design of the three-decker may have been empirical, but empiricism produces very good results after three centuries of evolution. Here was a timber structure, 180 ft long by 50 ft wide and 50 ft deep which could hold the sea in almost any weather, blockade French ports for two years on end or absorb huge punishment in battle. The framework could withstand the simultaneous recoil of fifty guns if need be, though they were more usually fired in a ripple. By balancing sail angles and wind against the water forces on the hull, it could sail close to the wind; and this, together with its broadside of guns, dictated the evolving tactics of sea battles. The sailing and armament of the ship were intimately linked with this evolution, from the clumsy movements of Stuart fleets to the swoops of that Mozart of naval warfare, Nelson, whose mastery of the rules allowed him to break them so confidently. The wooden three-decker was too good a design to be abandoned lightly by a nation which adored its navy.

From the seventeenth century onwards, concern was frequently expressed over the difficult supply of home-grown timber, but in fact the navy suffered little. The wooden three-decked ship of the line was not replaced by iron-armoured ships until 1860, and this was after two centuries of so-called timber shortage. There was a far more pressing reason for change—the new exploding shells. These had been invented in 1819 by Colonel Paixhans, but the long period of peace following the Napoleonic Wars had led to them being adopted gradually without being used in action between major powers. Earlier guns, the 32-pounder cannon, for instance, fired solid cast-iron balls which made 6-in diameter holes in ship's sides; the shot killed sailors and destroyed masts or rigging, but they seldom sank a ship in battle. Wooden ships were strong and shot holes were easily plugged, so that losses came chiefly from capture or storms. However, when the Russians fired the exploding shells at a Turkish fleet in November 1853 at Sinope, a new era began. The shells shattered the wooden sides of the Turkish vessels and only one escaped. The wooden capital ship was doomed, for protection could only be had with wrought iron armour. 'Any Ministry who should send wooden ships of the line to sea to oppose invulnerable iron ships would deserve impeachment.'[42] Even so, the first British armoured ship, *Warrior*, carried 18 in of teak backing to absorb the shock of hits on the 4-in wrought iron plating. The *Lord Clyde* and *Lord Warden* of 1864 had a total of 34 in of oak behind their 6-in armour, and wood backing continued in use until 1894. The Majestic class of 1895 was the first to dispense with wood and then, alas, one of them (the *Illustrious*) was rammed and pierced accidentally in its thinnest parts by a picquet boat, and consequently the steel ships were covered by a coat of thick wooden planking.

Iron also replaced wood rapidly in merchant ships. Less than one-tenth of the British tonnage built in 1850 was iron; by 1875, it was nine-tenths. The change did away with fears that shipbuilding might be transferred to countries with good timber supplies, but it would not have taken place without the demonstrable superiority of iron ships. Oak was only one-ninth the density of iron but one-tenth as strong, yet wooden structures had to be designed with twice the safety factor allowed in iron. By 1870, the hull took up between 35 and 45 per cent of the loaded displacement of a wooden ship but only 30–35 per cent in an iron ship — hence a much greater carrying capacity. On wooden warships the hull took up 50 per cent of the displaced weight, but this was barely improved in the first iron ones. It was the joints, not the strength of wood itself, which gave iron the advantage. Wooden structures had less integrity. The wooden keel had to be scarfed together from several timbers and the joints were always a weakness. The planks were laid separately and joined only to the framing, whereas the plating of an iron ship was so connected by rivets that the hull would have been strong even with the framing removed. Brunel's iron *Great Britain* was cast ashore in Ireland and survived months of pounding from the sea which would have destroyed any wooden hull. Iron ships were strong independent beams even without the support of the water, and they could be given double skins and watertight bulkheads to increase their safety. Finally, iron could better withstand the pounding of the engines which in wooden vessels 'was very trying and injurious to the structures'.[43]

The victory of iron was rapid and it would seem that technical considerations were more important than material shortages. Yet even a future Chief Naval Constructor, William White, who had plumped heavily for iron, could point to the wonderful performances of clippers like the *Melbourne* which had been known to log over 300 miles on each of seventeen consecutive days. When a model of *Cutty Sark* was tested in a ship tank it was found that at 16.5 knots — well below her fastest speed — she was drawing the equivalent of 4,000 indicated horsepower from the wind. As efficient compound engines and cheap coal made sail dispensable for long voyages, and the Suez Canal shortened steamship distances, so the advantages of the wooden sailing ship, with its romance, danger and discomfort, diminished. The nineteenth-century shipwright did not have the adhesives, plywoods and other fixings which have now transcended the weak joints known to him. Yet even today the story is not finished, as rising fuel costs may dictate speed reductions for engine-powered ships. Perhaps control engineering and aerodynamics applied to sail may produce a new kind of sailing ship which could compete in some branches of trade.

Before leaving the subject of ships, one more point needs to be made about the ultimate wooden designs. Not only were they beautiful aesthetically, but they were also classics of engineering. Their builders had endowed the three-deckers, clippers and frigates with the combination of range, manœuvrability, speed or carrying capacity which their service demanded. The high evolution of the eighteenth-century ship of the line contrasts strongly with the uncertainty of the armoured steam designs which followed. The English battlefleet between 1860 and 1880 was notoriously a fleet of samples, and odd samples at that. Perhaps the definitive form of the modern battleship was not reached until the Queen Elizabeth class of 1911. This quality of perfected design, within the vocabulary permitted by wood, is worth emphasizing whatever the simple advantages of length, strength and power conferred by iron. Such plain technical advantages have to be worked on before they attain a refinement which can be called classical.

Aircraft

Wooden aeroplane construction is a neglected topic. The originators of new metal structures, like Junkers, Short or Barnes Wallis can surely receive their due without muffling the importance of wood during the first twenty or even forty years of aviation. The first fliers — the Wrights, Bleriot, A. V. Roe and their contemporaries — had little choice; wood and bamboo were quite adequate for lightly-stressed structures, and were also cheap and easy to fabricate. Steel and aluminium fabrication would have cost too much for most pioneers to use. The situation was different during the Great War of 1914–18: aviation developed into a major industry; 55,093 airframes were manufactured in Britain during the war, at a rate of 2,668 monthly by 1918; and these aeroplanes were built of wood.[44] This was not a haphazard, improvised system but a national effort conducted by talented engineers. The aircraft built in this period had their main structural members, struts, spars and longerons in timber, and at major connecting points ingenious metal fastenings were used instead of wood joints which would weaken the system. Rigidity was achieved by steel-wire crossbracing, and it was a rigger's job to set this at the correct tension. These aircraft were a most successful example of the composite use of wood and metal. Farnborough and several university departments investigated aircraft construction materials and, even without urgency given by war, the Royal Naval Air Service and the Royal Flying Corps were keen enough rivals to insist on having the best equipment. The research was summarized in a report after the Armistice, which concluded that: 'Timber has held its position up to the end of the war as the best material for spars, struts, longerons and many other parts of aeroplanes owing to its remarkable strength and lightness.'[45]

This wartime research had put wood on to a new footing. For the first time it had been carefully investigated as an engineering material suited to scientific design. Wood suited the conditions of aviation which demanded lightness and strength with reasonable stiffness, and simplicity of manufacture. 'The conditions in which timber is used in aeroplanes are very different from those in any other engineering structure. Timber is rarely used in machines and experience of its properties is mainly confined to its use in buildings, ships, docks, scaffolding etc, where it is used in large sizes and where its exact strength is not important. Its use in aeroplanes is most analogous to its use in furniture, but there again no calculations of strength are needed. In aeroplane construction it is used in relatively small sections in the form of columns and beams, the strength of which must be subject to accurate calculation.'[46] Different species of timber were tested in tension, sheer, compression and under shock; along the grain and also tangentially and radially. The properties of spruce — exceptionally light, strong and straight-grained — commended it for most parts of the structure but ash or hickory were chosen for components more liable to shock. A spruce tension member will stand 20,000 lb per square inch before breaking. The cellulose tubes buckle more easily in compression, but still compare favourably, weight for weight, with many steels. Stiffness was another of wood's favourable qualities, even though it was poorer in absolute terms than steel or alloy. If we take its stiffness (the ratio of stress to strain, Young's Modulus) and divide it by the density, then spruce comes out rather better than the steels and light alloys used before 1939. It was hard to design strength and stiffness into metal wing spars and fuselages so as to compete with the lightness and simplicity of wood. After all, early aircraft flew at speeds not so different from the winds which trees have resisted for millions of evolutionary years.

Design conditions changed between the wars. Research on fuels and engines brought higher speeds, so wing loadings increased. The generally higher performance and weight of aeroplanes brought the compact strength of metal into its own. Hugo Junkers and Oswald Short were isolated pioneers of metal construction in 1918; by the 1930s all-metal aircraft like the Dakota and Spitfire seemed to foretell complete victory. Even so, there were still advantages to wood as late as 1940. F. T. Hill pointed out that wooden structures needed fewer parts than metal ones and were easier to repair without factory spares.[47] It might be easier to expand the production of metal aircraft in wartime, but on the other hand spruce was cheap and not used for much except aircraft.[48] It is worth noting that the same thing had also been argued against wooden ships, that the long seasoning of timber meant that it could not respond to sudden increases in demand. There was one difference between wooden ships and aircraft, however: iron ships lasted longer than wooden ones as a rule; but even if wooden aircraft were similarly short-lived, it did not matter since aircraft so rapidly became obsolete. Still, the future of large, high-performance aircraft seemed to lie with the aluminium alloys.

Yet, once again, wood showed its resilience. Throughout its history, craftsmen had wrestled with the difficulties of making strong joints, overcoming the weakness across the grain and wood's propensity to swell with moisture. Indeed, they had often made a virtue of necessity — planks swollen across the grain made a ship watertight, and flexible structures were stronger than rigid ones. It had also been known for a long time that the weakness across the grain could be countered by gluing thin veneers so as to cross their grain; but the early attempts failed through the treacherous inadequacies of bone and blood glues which softened and rotted under all save ideal conditions.[49] The 1920 Aeronautical Research Committee report saw that the 'ideal glue should be strong, adhere to all sorts of timber, resist moisture (hot and cold), not perish in dry heat, resist fungus and bacteria, be unaffected by fireproofing chemicals, and be easy to apply'.[50] By 1939, the new epoxy resins and thermosetting glues met these requirements and plywoods with high strength and reliability came into use. These in turn led to that legendary aircraft, the Mosquito. Here was a wooden aircraft which could absorb the power of its two Merlin engines, carry two tons of bombs over long ranges and fly faster than the best German propeller-driven fighters. It was used for bombing, photographic reconnaissance, long-range day-fighting, night-fighting and ground attack. It was also, like all de Havilland designs, very beautiful. Less beautiful, but also important, were the Horsa gliders, Bailey bridges and multitudinous naval applications which used the new plywoods. In 1942, Britain manufactured 55,000,000 square feet of aircraft plywood — two square miles of it![51]

Conclusions

What generalizations can we draw about the place of wood in technology since the Industrial Revolution? Scarcity does not seem to have been the critical problem, for although home supplies were deficient in quality, world production of timber met the demands. This is not to say, of course, that it was always easy to get the right wood when it was needed; wood was more troublesome to use than iron, and time spent on care and selection cost money. Furthermore, the scarcity reason does not fit the evidence from shipbuilding, civil engineering and aircraft. The replacement of wood by iron in bridges appears to be more related to new structural forms in wrought iron than to any other factor. In ships, too, the changing conditions of naval warfare seem to have been decisive in bringing about the change from wood. As an engineering material in general, wood retained its position while loadings, power and rotational speeds were low. It was happy with water and wind, but less so as steam engines grew bigger. As a natural material, wood was not adapted to modern forces like high-pressure steam or explosives. Wood, too, did not lend itself to very large structures. Ships up to 200 ft long were possible in simple timber, but the 700 ft of the *Great Eastern* could only be built in iron. It was the same with Stephenson's and Brunel's great bridges. Once stiff wrought iron structures had arrived, ductility and the convenience of rolled sections gave the new iron an advantage in bridge and ship design. Yet even as wrought iron itself was giving way to steel in ships, wood reappeared in aircraft. The low stresses and overriding need for lightness made wood the dominant material in aviation for more than twenty years. Perhaps the 420 ft long Schutte Lanz airships were the largest wooden structures ever to be built. Plywoods improved on the properties of plain timber and it is ironical that the first all-iron battleship, *Warrior*, framed in iron because of the injurious vibration of the steam engines, had only 1,250 horsepower — just half that of the de Havilland Mosquito.

We may distinguish three phases in the use of wood. First there was the age of pre-scientific craftsmen, who lacked power tools and modern fastenings; they cooperated with wood, using time and the grain of timber to achieve their ends. Secondly came a less sensitive phase, when post-scientific engineers used wood as a pre-scientific material. As we have seen, it survived with shipwrights and civil engineers, but for the mechanical engineer, wood was anathema to the ideals of precision, power and production. It disappeared quickly from the construction of machine tools, and when we compare wooden things made by wheelwrights or carpenters with wooden goods made by machinery it is as though we are comparing different materials, for the necessities of the machine degraded the possibilities that lay in a piece of timber. This was where industrialization hit wood the hardest. But, lastly, there came the phase where wood itself became a scientific material and competed on different terms. Plywoods, glues and other fastenings, together with engineering knowledge and improved industrial design, have placed wood on a new footing, though it is hard to generalize. For house roofs it is cheaper; for cricket bats it is better; for table tops it is a question of customer's choice. How, for instance, can one analyse the Mosquito? One can quantify performance, cost and its engineering properties; but what part was played by the genius of de Havilland, the tactical needs of the RAF, or by Britain's strategic commitment to a bombing offensive against Germany? Such reasons for the success of the aircraft are so disparate that one cannot arrive at an analysis claiming to be more scientific than intuitive. It is equally hard to compare wood, metal and plastics today. Few engineers are taught to use wood, and designers generally turn first to metal and plastics. Partly this may be economics, but one suspects that it may also be partly a fashion for using new materials.

Certainly, we have not yet heard the end of the story. The coming shortage of raw materials, especially plastics, will make wood an attractive alternative because it is a renewable resource. We have become accustomed to thinking of the last two centuries as the age of industrialization; perhaps it would be more useful to think of them as the age of fossil resources. The developing crisis in energy could mean that aircraft and ships travel more slowly so that wood's characteristics may become more attractive. Even mechanical engineers, whose call for precision constituted the arch-enemy of wood, may change. Much of the need for precision stems from the gears and linkages which transmit information, not energy. We are going to see electronics, especially the micro-chip, replace many of these mechanical control and informatic functions. Perhaps as rigid forms and linkages become less necessary, we shall find a new kind of machinery cross-bred from electronics and wood, just as the Mosquito was born out of the new chemical glues and birch veneers. In any new situation, much depends on individuals exploring a broad range of possibilities; luck, too, must play a part since we usually have to make decisions on a basis of imperfect information.[52] We can only guess the future uses of wood, but its history shows that it has remarkable qualities and that new methods and uses have continued to appear. The least one can say is that wood is a material which should never be ignored.

Notes

I wish to thank the following for their help while I was preparing this article: Dr A. W. D. Hills, Department of Metallurgy; T. Popple, E. Pritchard and E. Hanson, Department of Craft and Design, at Sheffield City Polytechnic; Jacques Raymond, Forester of Ayrens in the Auvergne; Dr N. J. Seeley, Department of Archaeological Conservation and Materials Science, University of London Institute of Archaeology; Sheffield Parks Department; and not least Geoffrey Howard and his staff at W. W. Howards Ltd, Bitterne Wharf, Southampton.

1. P. Deane, *The First Industrial Revolution*, Cambridge University Press, 1965, pp. 129–30. See also P. Mantoux, *The Industrial Revolution in the Eighteenth Century*, Methuen, London, 1964, pp. 306–10.

2. J. E. Gordon, *New Science of Strong Materials*, Penguin Books, Hardmondsworth, 1971, p. 122. *The International Book of Wood*, ed. M. Bramwell, Mitchell Beazley, London, 1976, pp. 226–7.

3. B. Franklin, 'Pennsylvanian Fire-places' in *The Works of Benjamin Franklin*, Longman, London, no date, Vol. II, p. 225.

4. M. W. Flinn, 'Timber and the Advance of Technology' in *Annals of Science*, Vol. 15, 1959, pp. 109–20.

5. *Encylopaedia Britannica*, 8th edition, 1860, article 'Timber', Vol. XXI, p. 268.

6. H. L. Edlin, *Know Your Broad Leaves*, HMSO, London, 1968, pp. 22–3.

7. H. D. Tiemann, *Wood Technology*, Pitman, London, 1951, pp. 367–72. A wide range of timbers give almost exactly half as much heat as the same weight of anthracite. Woods commonly burned range enormously in density, from 20 to 50 lb per cubic foot, while anthracite weighs about 90 lb per cubic foot.

8. J. E. Gordon, as note 2, pp. 138–43.

9. *Encyclopaedia Britannica*, Supplement to the 4th edition, 1824, Vol. V, p. 119, article 'Iron Making'.

10. *Encyclopaedia Britannica*, 3rd edition, 1797, article 'Tree', Vol. 18, p. 561.

11. M. W. Flinn, as note 4, p. 116.

12. J. Evelyn, *Sylva*, London, 1664, pp. 84–7.

13. The Society for the Encouragement of Arts, Manufactures and Commerce offered prizes each year for the largest new plantations of many species of trees, and also prizes to encourage saw-mills. See, for example, *Trans. Soc. for Encouragement of Arts, Manufactures, and Commerce*, 1783, Vol. I, pp. 41, 65–81; 1785, Vol. III, pp. 3–4, 222–39; 1791, Vol. IX, pp. 3–24, 199–200.

14. 'Home and Foreign Timbers' in *Mechanics Magazine*, Vol. XVII, 9 June 1832, p. 164.

15. A. C. Forbes, *The Development of British Forestry*, Arnold, London, 1910, p. 17.

16. R. Meiggs, *Home Timber Production 1939–1945*, Crosby Lockwood and Son, London, 1949, p. 117.

17. B. Latham, *Timber; an historical survey*, Harrap, London, 1957, pp. 23–51.

18. 'The Timber Trade, 1852' in *Mechanics Magazine*, Vol. LVIII, 15 Jan 1853, p. 48.

19. *Encyclopaedia Britannica*, 8th edition, 1860, article 'Timber', Vol. XXI, p. 278.

20. There are many other properties in wood, often used by craftsmen. Heartwood is stronger in compression, while sapwood is best in tension. The Tudor longbows recovered from the wreck of the *Mary Rose* have the heartwood of the yew at the back of the bow and the sapwood on the convex side.

21. This is necessarily a brief general account of the structure and behaviour of wood. Some useful books are: F. W. Jane, *The Structure of Wood*, Black, London, 1970; A. F. Rayne, 'The Investigation of Failures in Wood by Microscopical Examination', Oct 1945, reprinted in *Wood*, HMSO, 1952, pp. 3–9, wartime research with interesting photographs; *The International Book of Wood*, ed. M. Bramwell, Mitchell Beazley, London, 1976; J. E. Gordon, *New Science of Strong Materials*, Penguin, 1968; J. E. Gordon, *Structures*, Penguin, 1978; A. Schwankl, *What Wood is That?*, Thames and Hudson, London, 1957, a practical guide illustrated with veneer samples of many woods; Karl Borgin, 'How Wood Fails Under Stress' in *New Scientist*, 21 Nov 1974.

22. G. Sturt, *The Wheelwright's Shop*, Cambridge, 1963. W. Rose, *The Village Carpenter*, Cambridge, 1937.

23. Appleton, *Dictionary of Mechanics*, New York, 1861, Vol. II, pp. 933–53.

24. F. W. Jane, as note 21, p. 274.

25. A. Rees, *Encyclopaedia*, London, 1819, article 'Millwork' (the pages in Rees are not numbered).

26. H. Edlin, *Know Your Broadleaves*, Forestry Commission, HMSO, 1968, p. 125.

27. C. Tomlinson, *Encyclopaedia of the Useful Arts*, London, 1854, article 'Wood', p. 1018.

28. L. T. C. Rolt, *Isambard Kingdom Brunel*, Pelican, 1957, pp. 230–4.

29. 'Great American Viaduct' in *Mechanics Magazine*, Vol. XXI, 27 Sept 1834, pp. 433–8.

30. T. Tredgold, *Elementary Principles of Carpentry*, London, 1840, pp. 126–57.

31. P. M. Bingham, *History of the Public Works Department, Ceylon 1796–1913*, Colombo, 1921, p. 194.

32. L. G. Booth, 'The development of laminated timber arch structures in Bavaria, France and England in the early nineteenth century' in *Journal of the Institute of Wood Science*, Vol. 5, No. 5, 1971, pp. 3–16.

33. L. G. Booth, 'Laminated Timber Arch Bridges in England and Scotland' in *Newcomen Society Transactions*, Vol. XLIV, 1971–2, pp. 1–22.

34. N. Pevsner, *Pioneers of Modern Design*, Pelican, Harmondsworth, 1960, p. 133. It is only fair to say that Pevsner is following the spirit of nearly all the writers of that time who ignored the important wood content of the Crystal Palace.

35. C. Tomlinson, as note 27, pp. xxxix–xlv.

36. E. Clark, *The Britannia and Conway Tubular Bridges*, 2 Vols, London, 1850. *Encyclopaedia Britannica*, 8th edition, 1860, article 'Iron Bridges' by Robert Stephenson, Vol. XII, pp. 607–10. Britannia must be counted among the world's outstanding bridges. Its demolition, following a fire, can only be a source of increasing regret that the bridge was not restored.

37. L. T. C. Rolt, *Tools for the Job*, Batsford, London, 1968, pp. 67–91.

38. J. E. Gordon, *Structures*, Penguin, 1978, p. 271.

39. N. Rosenberg, ed., *The American System of Manufacture, 1854–5*, Edinburgh University Press, 1969.

40. 'The Invention of Wood-cutting Machinery, Sir Samuel Bentham — Mr. Brunel' in *Mechanics Magazine*, Vol. LVI, 3 April 1852, p. 271.

41. The literature on the wooden ship is enormous: C. Cipolla, *Guns and Sails*, Collins, London, 1965; William Falconer, *Marine Dictionary*, London, 1780, reprinted David and Charles, Newton Abbot, 1970; M. Lewis, *The Navy of Britain*, Allen and Unwin, London, 1948; C. Nepean Longridge, *The Anatomy of Nelson's Ships*, MAP, Hemel Hempstead, 1955; *Encyclopaedia Britannica*, in all editions from the third to the eighth, carries excellent articles on seamanship, shipbuilding, tactics and war. The Hornblower novels of the late C. S. Forester are, of course, essential reading.

42. Quoted in O. Parkes, *British Battleships*, Seeley Service, London, 1966, p. 49. See also J. W. King, *Warships and Navies of the World*, Boston, 1881, pp. 59–60, and also H. W. Wilson, *Ironclads in Action*, Sampson Low, London, 1896, Vol. I, p. xxxi.

43. W. H. White, *Manual of Naval Architecture*, Murray, London, 1877, pp. 363–406.

44. H. Penrose, *British Aviation: the Great War and Armistice, 1915–1919*, London, Putnam, 1969, pp. 448–9.

45. Aeronautical Research Committee, *Report on Materials of Construction used in Aircraft and Aircraft Engines*, HMSO, London, 1920, p. 95.

46. *Ibid.* For comparison, see the article 'Strength of Materials' by John Robison in *Encyclopaedia Britannica*, 3rd edition, which gives very varying figures for the strengths of the species of timbers. There are much fuller experiments under the same heading in Rees, 1819, see note 25. However, as W. H. White makes clear, there was always a tendency to overdesign in wood.

47. F. T. Hill, *Materials of Aircraft Construction*, Pitman, London, 1940, pp. 274–276.

48. Further research was done on timber during the Second World War. There was not enough spruce, so American Whitewood, Western Hemlock, Kara Redwood (Scots pine) and Douglas fir were tested as substitutes, though all had to be of higher density to compare with spruce in strength. When speaking of scientific design in wood, it must be remembered how much samples vary. Grade A spruce, with a density above 24 lb a cubic foot, varied in tensile strength from 19,600 lb/sq in to 23,500 with an average of 20,200; but after twenty-five years' experience with spruce, designers knew that they had a material which gave little trouble. See *Wood*, HMSO, 1952, pp. 3–46.

49. J. E. Gordon, *New Science of Strong Materials*, Penguin, 1968, pp. 144–50.

50. Aeronautical Research Committee, see note 45, pp. 121–2.

51. A. D. Wood, *Plywoods of the World*, Johnston and Bacon, Edinburgh, 1963, p. 189.

52. A similar comment is made by J. M. Coles, S. V. E. Heale and B. J. Orme, 'The use and character of wood in prehistoric Britain and Ireland' in *Proceedings of the Prehistoric Society*, Vol. 44, December 1978, pp. 1–2. It is interesting to note in their analysis of wooden artefacts that twenty-seven of the spear shafts examined were made of ash and only twelve from other timber (p. 25). One wonders whether the average civilized man would know why this was a good choice.

Francis Bacon and the Myth of Industrial Science

MICHAEL FORES

I. Introduction

Many commentators on the subject believe that there has been a step-change in the way that useful, bulky artefacts are made, this having occurred either at the time of 'the industrial revolution'; or, perhaps, it occurred in a 'technological revolution' which took place sometime in the eighteenth or the nineteenth centuries, in those parts of the world which were the most 'developed' at the time. With such an account of change, one interpretation is Farrington's of Francis Bacon's prophetic vision having come true:

> The idea is a commonplace today, partly realized, partly tarnished, still over misunderstood; but in his day it was a novelty. It is simply that knowledge ought to bear fruit in works, that science ought to be applicable to industry, that men ought to organize themselves as a sacred duty to improve and transform the conditions of life.[1]

Bernal agreed with this line of thinking; and Cardwell has suggested that Bacon was 'the advocate and prophet, if not the originator, of the movement that was to establish technology ... on the foundations of technics and science'. Then there is Pursell's and Kranzberg's argument that:

> At the beginning of the 19th century the wedding of science to technology had been a philosopher's ideal, based on Francis Bacon's notions of two centuries earlier; but by the beginning of the 20th the marriage had been consummated and its offspring were increasingly numerous.[2]

With this interpretation, many commentators have also thought it suitable to quote Whitehead's assessment about changes that took place in the nineteenth century:

> What is peculiar and new to the century, differentiating it from all its predecessors, is its *technology*. It was not merely the introduction of some great isolated inventions. It is impossible not to feel that something more was involved.

Technical change speeded up, according to Whitehead, becoming 'quick, conscious and expected'. Furthermore:

> The greatest invention of the nineteenth century was the invention of the method of invention. A new method entered into life. ... The prophecy of Francis Bacon has now been fulfilled; and man, who at times dreamt of himself as a little lower than the angels, has submitted

to become the servant and the minister of nature. . . . The whole change has arisen from the new scientific information.[3]

So there is a picture built up, by a number of commentators, which is akin to Mumford's belief that science, and not necessity, is now the mother of invention.[4] Thus, science is often made to appear, too, in the role of the mother of material prosperity, or at least as prosperity's grandmother.

An examination of the detailed evidence, however, and of the causal linkages implied, or stated, in the line of argument sketched out here shows that much is wrong with it. As Rossi has pointed out, Bacon's principal aim was not to found a new sort of 'industrial science', whatever that phrase may mean. Instead, Bacon was keen to establish a type of written-down science, a 'natural philosophy', which was backed by observation, rather than being simply a body of philosophizing about events in the abstract. For Purver:

> According to Bacon's plan for 'the New Philosophy' a 'History of Nature' had to be compiled, constituting the Phenomena of the Universe; that is to say, experience of every kind, and such a natural history as may serve for a foundation to build philosophy upon.[5]

Bacon, later a hero to the 'rationalists', even claimed that his vision for science was against 'reason': that science should have more to do with inquiry than with speculation, more to do with observation than with creating fine phrases in accounts:

> For we are founding a real model of the world in the understanding, such as it is found to be, not such as man's reason has distorted. Now this cannot be done without dissecting and anatomizing the world most diligently; but we declare it necessary to destroy completely the vain little, and as it were, apish imitations of the world, which have been formed in various systems of philosophy by men's fancies.[6]

In this paper, I aim to do three things: sketch out further what Bacon's central preoccupation really was in the context of the state of the science of his time; argue that the idea of 'industrial science' is, like that of 'applied science', inappropriate and confusing — the construction of each phrase is linked to a denial of one of the main characteristics of science; question further whether there was the 'revolution' in technical practice referred to before. Overall, the paper is written in the post-Baconian tradition of linking observation to the record, which is suitable for present purposes. Further, it is philosophical in temper, in Whitehead's sense of being concerned to criticize abstractions: 'You cannot think without abstractions; accordingly it is of the utmost importance to be vigilant in critically revising your methods of abstraction.'[7]

The second listed issue is covered in section II — ideas of 'pure science', 'applied science', 'empirical science' and 'industrial science' have been amongst those artefacts of record that have confused the layman, not only about science, but about the technical activities. The first listed issue is covered in section III; Bacon was, in fact, arguing for the opposite of what many of his would-be followers imagine to be the case — for a kind of 'pure science', in present usage. In section IV, it is argued that there was no change of the type that might be called 'scientification' in the eighteenth century or the nineteenth century; nor can there ever be because of the division of labour between men and machines. The last section raises a more general issue, briefly about error through scholarship and in 'the professorial style'. For, if the word 'technology' is substituted for 'nature' in the following passage, my complaint is well summarized by Bacon himself:

> They who have presumed to dogmatize on nature [and on the so-called 'technology'], as on some well investigated subject, either from self-conceit or arrogance, and in the professorial style, have inflicted the greatest injury on philosophy and learning. For they have tended to stifle and interrupt inquiry exactly in proportion as they have prevailed in bringing others to their opinion; and their own activity has not counterbalanced the mischief they have occasioned by corruption and destroying that of others.[8]

This paper, then, is part of a wider story of 'mischief' made,[9] where a sense of scholarly 'discipline' and form, and the effects of man-made systems of constructing records, have got in the way of a quest for the truth — even on the topic that 'science', presumably to do with the truth, 'ought to be applicable to industry'.

II. 'Industrial Science' and 'Applied Science'

English-language science is a feast more moveable than Easter, providing a major problem for those who want to discuss it in the critical mode. Sometimes it turns up in spring as written-down, tested knowledge of things observed. Sometimes it can be found coming in summer, as a method or a process of work: 'Science tells us X or Y or Z.' Then, there is autumnal science, too: that of the 'two cultures', the one eternally opposed to the other — though I shall argue later that the exercise of scientific inquiry is patently an art. Come winter, science may adopt another guise: it can be the spirit of the times, as in the phrase 'the Age of Science', something sent to keep its adherents warm through periods of war, natural disaster and rising price of fuel. It is in winter, or perhaps in autumn, that, in Farrington's phrase, 'men ought to organize themselves as a sacred duty to improve and transform the conditions of life'.

This paper is so organized itself that the word 'science' only has one meaning, that of springtime and the season of new hopes, being the principal output of what German speakers know as *wissenschaftlich* inquiry. It is the book of tested knowledge of things observed; and mathematics has no part in it except as a language used, like Spanish or Latin or English, to help to bridge the gap between observation and record. Because of the special qualities of this springtime science, any attempts are misplaced to tack an adjective of qualification to the word, if the user of such a constructed phrase wants his comment to be dealt with in the critical and testing manner of scientific discourse. Because of its importance in the world, it is prudent to tie down the meaning of science; as a dog is a dog and not a mouse.

Science, then, is a public good which has the special quality that, when it is passed from person to person, there is no change in its stock or condition. Researcher A tells Researcher B what he knows about Topic C, often in the hope that B will test what he has been told, to see if he judges that what he hears (Finding D) is as close to the truth as possible. The sharing of Finding D between A and B does not mean that A no longer knows this. There is not a similar condition of change as, when Unit R wants to get hold of some private knowledge that is in the possession of Unit S, due to the fact that Individual T is the only one who 'knows' it, R is forced to hire T to Unit S's detriment. The transaction from A to B is not, either, like that when a penny passes hands — either to be borrowed or to be spent. Simply, when Finding D passes hands from A to B, in an act that the pundits may like to call 'a knowledge-transfer process', the same package of knowledge is with B as had been before with A; and none is deprived of Finding D if A or B tells Researcher E as well.

Finding D may well be modified later, it is true, after test or more inquiry; but it does not change its form on transfer, sharing or acquisition. With the shifts of knowledge between A and B, between A and E, and between B and E, nothing has happened of the type that is implied by the use of the past participle in these phrases: a fallen leaf, a bent pin, a spent penny, a battered baby, a worn brake-pad — all being phrases that are built up using a noun that describes something that is a 'scarce good' in the economists' phrase (that is to say, such goods *do* change their stock or condition on transfer from one to another).

What, then, can 'applied science' mean, when science itself has such a quality that when it passes hands, nothing happens to it of the type of falling, bending, spending and the rest? From the construction of the phrase, the hearer might expect that the science that had been 'applied' — to what? — had changed its form; why use a past participle otherwise? Of course, scientific knowledge can be put to use in 'practice' and for more on this last notion, see the last section of the paper. But the reason for bothering to distinguish a 'used car' from an 'unused car' is to stress the difference between them. If the caption to a famous political cartoon had said, 'would you buy an *un*used car from this man?', the issue raised would have been quite a different one from that raised by asking, 'would you buy a *used* car from him?' A used car is expected to have quite different qualities from one that has not been used by a previous owner. A battered baby has undergone a change of condition with the experience of being battered. But science used is constrained to be exactly the same as science unused. Or perhaps the change that is meant to have taken place between, say, 'pure science' and 'applied science' is of a different type completely? — the 'science' of the first of the two phrases is knowledge, that of the second is something else?

The simple model of 'knowledge transfer' for science proper that is sketched out here works in much the same way if Researcher A shares his Finding D with Non-researcher F, as if he shared it with B, or if it was B who told F about Finding D. A will perhaps be keener to let B or E know what he has found out, simply because of the nature of science (that is, springtime science). Few will believe A about Topic C, unless others known as 'scientists' have been given a chance to test A's work; and researchers are more likely to do this than non-researchers. But it still makes no difference to Finding D who hears about it first. It remains the same finding, with test being a separate act from transfer. And the use (perhaps, by an engineer) of Finding D, in the arena that many call 'practice', will not normally lead to a change in the finding either.

There are some who make a claim that an engineer is well described as an 'applied scientist' because he makes use of ideas such as Newton's Laws of Motion in the course of his work. But the irony of this choice of phrase lies with two facts. The 'purest' of the 'pure' in science, and the most 'basic' of the 'basic', often turn out to be the most applicable to use, and so too the most 'applied' to use. Due to the special quality of science, 'pure science' is constrained to be exactly the same as 'applied science' — unless, of course, 'science' has skipped around in meaning between the two phrases.

Given the weakness of the phrase 'applied science', to inform on the transfer of knowledge for use, and given that scientists, cooks, engineers and housewives all make use of scientific knowledge freely in their work, what of the construct 'industrial science'? There is an obvious difficulty with this verbal construction because of the issue raised before about attempts to use adjectives to qualify the noun 'science'. Scientists seek to describe generally and universally. So, assuming that the meaning of science here is the springtime one (knowledge of things observed), there may be a 'Mexican ant', a 'Spanish fly' or an 'American flag'; but there is no 'American science' as opposed to 'Mexican science', no 'happy science' as opposed to 'sad science', no 'yellow science' as opposed to 'pink science'. Indeed, even the phrases of convenience, which seem to set a boundary between such things as 'physical science' and 'biological science', are rather bogus. For everyone is found looking at the same world, whereas parts of that world do not appear in packages with labels on them saying 'biology', 'physics', 'anthropology', 'economics', 'history'. Biologists study living things that are made up of physical matter. Often exactly the same features of the same man-made world are called 'economic' by those who see themselves to be economists, 'social' by the sociologists, and so on.

Now, take the use of something like Ohm's Law in the place that is called 'industry', somewhere with widespread and indistinct boundaries.[10] This is exactly the same proposition if it is used by a farmer to help him put up a fence to keep his cattle in a restricted area, or if it is used by a householder to help him install a ring-main at home. Engineers make use of Ohm's Law as well, to be sure, when they are working in factories; though it is often virtually 'second nature' to them.

Can this same proposition be sensibly known as a part of 'industrial science' when it is used by engineers, as a part of 'agricultural science' when used by a farmer, and as a part of 'domestic science' when it is used at home? For those who would answer 'yes', I ask them simply what they will call (the same) Ohm's Law when a natural scientist uses it in his laboratory — 'scientific science'? That would be a new phrase to me, but at least one that has been constructed in the spirit of the other three. Certainly the phrases 'agricultural science' and 'domestic science' make some sense when used to designate teaching programmes. But the adoption of each helps to mask the fact that none owns science in the manner that scarce goods are owned. Student engineers and student physicists each learn of Ohm's Law and so who is to say whether it is best classed as a part of 'physics', or perhaps 'technology', or perhaps 'engineering science'?

Here, it is enough to stress that science is science and not a bowl of cherries. Also, boundaries set up within the book of science have doubtful legitimacy. They are the same propositions ('laws', perhaps) and the same findings (such as Finding D above) that are in use wherever they are used. What is held to be 'basic' in science may well be simply a matter of taste and particular convenience. Newton's Laws of Motion are important to engineers, but to nuclear physicists they are incorrect. I will argue later that the phrases 'empirical science' and 'experimental science' are just as misconceived and confusing as 'applied science' and 'industrial science'.

For Farrington, Bacon was the 'philosopher of industrial science' because his vision was that of 'a marriage between natural philosophy and industrial production ... between science and industry'.[11] The question of Bacon's vision is dealt with more extensively in the next section of this paper. Up to now the invariable nature of scientific knowledge has been stressed, on its transfer, or on its use in 'practice'. Could the main ideas of 'industrial science' and 'applied science' be associated, then, with some other meaning of the word 'science' than that which makes it recorded knowledge (springtime science)?

These two phrases seem to have been adopted for use in English for the discussion of aspects of the so-called 'industrial era', to imply that there has been a step-change in technical practice in manufacturing and other locations. Before the 'marriage' noted, this viewpoint seems to say that technical activity was 'trial-and-error' or 'craft' or 'empirical' in type; afterwards, 'science' had so influenced technical practice that it can be dubbed 'scientific' in type.[12] This is the idea to be examined in the fourth section of this paper; here I will concentrate only on one consequence of using 'science' in both the summertime and springtime senses in the same treatments.

Common sense suggests, and familiarity with these activities supports it, that, just because the technical specialist knows more about the materials that he is using in some era dubbed 'industrial', because it is thought to be distinctively 'modern', this does not mean that he has changed his ways of working in some fundamental manner. Just because scientists have evolved some techniques of inquiry by experiment, measurement and the use of mathematics, there is no evidence to indicate that these are exclusively 'scientific' in some well-labelled way. Production bosses do experiments, carpenters measure, financial accountants use mathematics without any of these people being described as 'scientists'. Nor, *a priori*, are the tricks of the trade of the scientists likely to be so very useful in technical activity. Scientists chop things up to see what is inside; technical specialists build anew. Scientific work is judged against the truth, technical work against utility. Research is the core activity for the scientist, design (something different in type) for the technical specialist. You do not change an engineer's spots by describing him anew as a 'scientist', perhaps in summer or autumn, when he was not one in spring.

What seems to have gone wrong is that, with the skip-over of 'science' from one meaning to another, those who think in terms of science as a process have become confused over what is often called 'scientific method'. Whereas, in fact, despite the continual use of that phrase there is no such thing that is discernible: there is no unique way of obtaining the findings that go together to form the book of science.[13] Partly because the *output* of the work of the scientists (springtime science) is so well tested, there is no need for them to adopt any particular and formalized mode of work to produce that output. Since, then, there is nothing that is readily recognizable as characteristically summertime science, or perhaps autumnal science in the usage adopted here, there is not much future in invoking non-scientists, such as the so-called 'technologists', to act in a 'scientific' manner. Such advice given rarely, if ever, tells anyone what to do next.[14]

III. Francis Bacon

It was said of Bacon, by the biologist Harvey, that he wrote of science like a Lord Chancellor. And Whitehead has suggested that 'Leonardo was more completely a man of science than was Bacon. The practice of naturalistic art is more akin to the practice of physics, chemistry and biology than is the practice of law.'[15] It takes some effort for most to grasp that, in the sixteenth and seventeenth centuries when Bacon lived, many features of life were different from those which we face today. This was, for instance, the age in which there were examples of multi-specialists, in the way of the ideal of the 'Renaissance man'. I believe that Whitehead is right to have made the point about Leonardo that is quoted. Although it must be stressed that he was employed for much of his working life as a military and civil engineer, it is fairly clear that Leonardo's observant eye served him in good stead in the two other activities of 'fine artist' and natural scientist. He seems to have been, in fact, the sort of close observer of nature that Bacon demanded for his new science:

> ... if anyone were desirous of examining and contemplating the talents and industry of an artificer, he would not merely wish to see the rude materials of his art, and then his work when finished, but rather to be present whilst he is at labor, and proceeding with his work. Something of the same kind should be done with regard to nature.[16]

Bacon then goes on to describe, in some detail, the germination of a seed in the ground. And it can be noted that his plea for close examination of the real working of artificers' skills is much the same as that which I made previously for an improved history of the making of useful artefacts.[17]

It would, however, be wrong to write down Bacon's role or influence simply in the terms indicated by Harvey and Whitehead. After all, he *was* Lord Chancellor of England and had lived most of his life at, or near, the court; so it was not so inappropriate that he was caught writing as a lawyer and a politician. Furthermore, as Purver comments in a history of the origins of the Royal Society of London, Bacon was above anything else a philosopher by intention, and a pioneer of a new type of scholarship against the traditions of the established universities; he was this, rather than someone who aimed to follow his own recommendations about the need for close observation of nature. As Rossi remarks, it was his 'plan for the reform of science [which] was his [Bacon's] great contribution to culture'. Following Purver again, Bacon preferred to classify according to bodies of knowledge 'for this would help to build up sciences themselves, which was of immeasurably greater importance than merely improving crafts or industries. . . .'[18]

Francis Bacon was born in London in 1561 in a country which was fairly backward compared with some of Continental Europe, but with a silver spoon in his mouth. His father was Sir Nicholas Bacon who was Queen Elizabeth's Lord Keeper, being virtually the chief political executive of the country. His uncle was the future Lord Burghley, who became the head of the most powerful political faction in the land. His mother was an educated woman; Bacon's was 'an appropriate home to be born into for the future master of eloquence in Latin and in English'.[19]

Bacon himself followed his father to Cambridge, where 'the lay Protestant officers of the State' of the new order 'were trained';[20] and subsequently he became a Member of Parliament at the early age of 23. Records suggest that Bacon was, apart from two years at the English Embassy in Paris, based in London for the rest of his life until the time of his dismissal from the office of Lord Chancellor for fraud in 1622. We are dealing with a very important figure, a high courtier from a successful family, who was virtually England's ruler when the King went back to his native Scotland on visits.

The most perceptive, and sympathetic, critics of Bacon's scientific impact make a case which is quite consistent with the kind of life which is sketched out in the previous paragraphs. As someone who was a courtier, it is much more likely that he would have taken up the role of philosopher than that of experimenter or observer of manufacturing processes. And indeed there was an enormous effort of persuasion to be done on that score, given the weight of ages of indifferent scholarly speculation which had become enshrined as wisdom.

At the time that Bacon took up his pen in passion, existing speculation about the characteristics of nature did not tie in at all well with close observation of events. The four medieval elements, earth, air, fire and water, for instance, were transmitted as beliefs and not closely linked with the results of experiments. Thus one summary of Bacon's standpoint[21] is that he had two basic ideas, the first of which comprises his major statement for the development of science:

(a) traditional learning must be replaced by the cult of nature so as to re-establish the contact between man and reality;

(b) collections of facts are a means of study, an instrument for scientific research and not objects of pleasure and curiosity.

As noted, Whitehead suggests that Bacon believed that man had 'submitted to become the servant and the minister of nature'. But this is not correct for the context of this restricted point and the main issue of this article: it must be stressed, instead, that Bacon's interest in the *use* of natural knowledge was secondary. The 'industrial arts' and the 'mechanical arts' of manufacture were not much exercised in the locations which he knew well; whereas, above all, he was a man to aim to practice what he preached as far as possible. And Bacon preached that personal experience and intellectual conjecture should be brought more closely together.

This is not to argue that Bacon was not interested at all in the utility of knowledge or in the importance of the exponents of the useful arts of manufacturing. On the contrary, and as Rossi points out, the viewpoint of his age differed from that accepted in many parts of the world today:

> The accomplishments of artisan, engineer, technician, navigator, and inventor were considered of equal importance to intellectual achievements, and Bacon, Galileo, and Harvey, amongst others, explicitly acknowledged their debt to the artisan.[22]

So there was indeed a link, accepted at the time, the opposite of that implied by the modern idea of 'applied science'. With this the body of science was taken to have developed with the benefit of help from the work of the artisan. And Bacon explicitly and consistently held up the example of the thriving 'mechanical arts' as being the home of the sorts of change which ought to take place if a proper science was to be produced. In contrast to 'particular systems of philosophy and the sciences ... which are founded on opinion' and rarely change:

> the case is reversed, in the mechanical arts, which are founded on nature and the light of experience, for they (as long as they are popular) seem full of life, and uninterruptedly thrive and grow, being at first rude, then convenient, lastly polished, and perpetually improved.[23]

They were what might be called the 'popular arts' of the day which allowed observation and abstraction to be brought together closely.

Bacon has been criticized latterly that he neglected measurement in favour of classification; that he backed 'the inductive method of eliciting general laws', calling for a scrap-book rather than an ordered record;[24] that 'he had no knowledge of or sympathy with the new mathematical philosophy'; that his method was 'largely negative', stressing the false trails of the past, and limitations to discovery such as in the human senses.[25] All such contentions (true or false) and speculations associated with them help the reader to miss the point that what Bacon was calling for was 'science for science's sake'; and this is further obscured by what is said of 'scientific method'.

It is a simple error of classification to call the process which produces science (summertime science, here) by the same name as its product (spring-time science). More crippling, however, is an outcome of this error which concerns the act by which the characteristics of science (as an intended rational, best explanation of observed events) seem to have been visited, in a host of accounts, on the scientist's specialist arts.[26] Thus, Popper and his followers make a claim that Bacon was wrong about 'scientific method'. Scientists are would-be falsifiers and not would-be verifiers; it is 'deduction' that is at the heart of this type of inquiry and not the 'induction' that Bacon wanted to see in use by scientists. That is to say, the Popperians argue that the most suitable rationalization on the process of scientific inquiry (sum-mertime science) is that generalizations about the observable world are not 'induced' from observations made in the way that the Baconians require. Rather, such propositions can derive from anywhere, are never finally true and are always prone to be shown up as false.[27]

The Popperians may be right for many cases of inquiry, but the argument set out before about mythic 'scientific method' is germane. The Popperians make a considerable show of distinguishing something that is 'non-science'. Otherwise put, some statements cannot sensibly be considered as a part of science (springtime science, in this paper). This is because: '*Falsifiability is the criterion of demarcation between science and non-science* ... only if it is testable is it scientific.'[28] Due to the facts that scientists tend to write down semi-fictitious accounts about how they do their work, and that none has the power to look into the heads of individuals at work to discern the details of how they operate, the Popperian notion of demarcation does not allow statements made about 'scientific method' to be classed as a proper part of 'science'. For all the discussion that there may have been of a 'revolution' from Bacon's time in the ways that scientists operate, we simply do not know how, or if, this may be. Very possibly, the active scientist will use induction on a Monday and deduction on a Tuesday. He will try to falsify general propositions on a Wednesday and verify them on a Thursday. On Friday and all the next week he will have his work cut out simply to make observations as best he can. And, luckily for the scientist, it rarely matters a jot how the mode of his working is described by others *ex post*. His work is an art, like that of other specialists of the species *homo faber*, as he plays his hunches and seeks to make judgements in circumstances where little is known.[29]

Since it is impossible to know the full set of methods of those whom we call 'scientists' today — those of pre- *and* post-Baconian times — the phrases 'experimental science' and 'empirical science' bite the dust, both for science as a product of work (springtime science) and for science as a process (summertime science). The labels 'applied science', 'pure science' and 'basic science' are as inappropriate for science as a process as they are for science proper (the product). Who can say with confidence why anyone does his work?

Finally, on Bacon's message to others, those commentators who have suggested that his work is best thought of in terms of 'industrial science' have misunderstood what he was trying to achieve. Bacon was not, as Rossi realizes, mainly a 'pioneer in the application of science in industry . . .'; and so he was not the type of prophet referred to in the introduction of the paper. Instead, he 'was putting up the modern ideal of scientific research in opposition to the traditional ideals of magic and alchemy'.[30] And he realized this himself. In the final remarks on a list of 'particular histories' (areas of science) that ought to be instituted, we can read of 130 items including: Heavenly Bodies; Rainbows; Air as a whole; Serpents, Worms, Flies, and other insects. We can also read clearly of Bacon's lack of a primary concern for manufacturing:

> It may not be amiss to observe that, whereas many of the experiments must come under more titles than one . . . it will be more convenient to investigate them with reference to Arts [in the study of human skills], and to arrange them with reference to Bodies [subject-matter]. For I care little about the mechanical arts themselves: only about those things which they contribute to the equipment of philosophy [formal knowledge].[31]

IV. The Myth of Technological Revolution

That said, I must assert that there is no body of detailed evidence to support the contention sketched out before in this paper, that there was a genuine discontinuity in technical practice in the leading countries of the world in the eighteenth or the nineteenth century.[32] Accordingly, the commentator who sets out to deal with this topic has a good deal of latitude available to him for how to try to refute the idea. Either he can state his case clearly and briefly, to challenge his potential critics to prove him wrong for he knows they will fail. Or he can state some evidence himself to support his position. Or he can seek to explain, in more philosophical terms, how such a revolution is impossible. Here, the last course is chosen in the main, along with some of the second, to expand on what the opposition's standpoint seems to be.

Thus, Schmookler is amongst the many commentators on the technical functions to have claimed that it is feasible and useful to distinguish a type of 'scientific invention' from that which is 'purely empirical'.[33] But such a distinction must loom less large when it is remembered that those who argue thus also tend to say that 'science' (the summertime one, the process) is itself 'empirical' in type in the era when 'scientific invention' takes place. If the notion of 'technological revolution' is taken away from this typing scheme and the scientific mode of work is recognized to be the art that it really is, scientists, inventors and other technical specialists can all be seen as those who use skill and written-down knowledge in indiscernible amounts in their work. As members of the tinkering species, *homo faber*, they are employed mainly for their skilful behaviour operating in conjunction with designerly

imagination. So Schmookler's distinction can be seen to stem from a confusion between necessary and sufficient conditions for inventive success. The
possession of scientific knowledge may be necessary to the designer and the
inventor alike, but this is not sufficient for him to do an adequate job of
work. He still has to tinker about in the 'empirical' mode in order to choose
between alternative outturns in circumstances where a 'best solution' is
rarely, if ever, apparent.[34]

Then Kuznets has associated his conception of a separable era of 'modern
economic growth', for which he was awarded a Nobel Prize in economics,
with the belief that: 'Modern industrialization is the product of modern
technology and science, a reflection of the marked additions to the stock of
useful knowledge ...' While Mumford has depicted the technical specialist
of recent times as typically a kind of hack, or perhaps a puppet pulled on a
string by science. Faraday is held to be the real inventor of the dynamo, not
Siemens; and so on. Lilley talks of a 'new phase' from some time in the
nineteenth century in the development of 'industrial civilization', where
'the future would lie with those individuals, those companies and those
nations who could make the best use of science'.[35] Nothing in this standpoint
can help the questioner even to start answering the query. If science is
formal, published knowledge of the observable world and engineering is
cast as something like 'the use of science' or 'the application of science in
practice', how is it that, with the same 'science' available to Engineer M
and Engineer N, each makes a different turbine to fill the same specified
needs? The 'best use of science' proposition simply cannot say. Nor can it
say why it is that, although the body of (springtime) science is continually
changing, the products of the so-called 'technology' do not invariably
change as a direct consequence. Some major and genuine shifts in understanding, such as with the overturning of the Newtonian system of mechanics
by Einstein, may make no discernible difference at all in some branches of
engineering. And the answer to the apparent paradox lies with pointing out
that the core designerly functions in technical work are always centrally
concerned with having to judge between alternative solutions to technical
problems, in a regime where very little is known compared with the ideal
conditions of 'ration decision-making' as they are outlined in the books on
'management'.[36]

Then, too, the author of a chapter on 'Industry' in *The New Cambridge
Modern History* has discussed 'the very slowness of *technical* change over
mankind's history, its spottiness, the lack of ready diffusion of its results', for
the period before the 'industrial revolution' in Britain. He has discussed
explicitly 'scientific and technical knowledge'. And of the 'industrial' era,
he writes that: '*Technological* change, at least before the age of the research
laboratory and a developed engineering and scientific base, depended upon
the unorganised ideas and obsessions of individual inventors.'[37] But, in
truth, the formalized knowledge that is sometimes known as 'technical' in
type is not distinct from that called 'scientific' (concerning nature): mechanics and thermodynamics form a part of each.[38] It is not apt to lay in the
hands of those called 'inventors' *all* of technical change; invention is defined

specifically as that which is *untypical* of such change. The slip-over in labelling from 'technological' to 'technical change', for periods each side of some watershed point, assumes that there was such a watershed without proving it. Then, who can be so sure that 'science' can be *'basic'* to technical practice in some way: or even that something called 'engineering' can fill that role? Certainly, a chair or a table can be seen to have its 'base' on the floor. But, for all the information that has been made available about the eighteenth-century and nineteenth-century 'relationships' between science and 'technology', we are not informed much about how the latter worked from this preoccupation. It might be more instructive to examine the links between technical specialists and farmers in that period for at least the first had to eat in order to achieve successful technical development. I shall argue subsequently that scientific knowledge cannot sensibly be thought of as being 'basic' to any type of 'practice' at work in any age. To believe that it can be is to misunderstand the nature of those tasks that are undertaken by men rather than by machines.[39]

The best way to deal with the issues raised so far in this section of the present paper is to follow through the contention that, just as there has been a division of labour between man and man, so there has been a division of labour between man and man-made machines. The link is always in flux, often unremarkable (as with the writer and his pen), and almost certainly as old as that more-discussed arrangement between man and man. If the 'pre-historians' are to be believed, it was man's ability to develop and use machines which was behind the rise of town-life that many call 'civilization'. For the skilful tool-using *homo faber* of the countryside was, at some stage, able to produce a surplus of food that made it possible for skilful tool-using *faber*-craftsmen to set up in the towns and specialize on the things that they could do best.

The division of labour is always guided by who, or what, is best at certain activities. Thus, what a machine does best is precisely that type of work that is often characterized as 'technological' in type for the era after the 'revolution' under discussion here. Machines are good at the 'application' of knowledge and principles 'to practical tasks' because of the ways that men have built them. While machines can be developed to undertake well-specified tasks effectively, man is particularly effective when it is not clear beforehand what has to be done. Men also get personal satisfaction from doing work in this last distinctively-human mode and have constantly praised each other for their ability to rise above the animals in confident effectiveness at making a range of artefacts.[40] Animal behaviour is instinctive only, we tend to tell each other; man is a good deal grander. But in what way?

If machines and the other animals besides man had the sensitivity and skill that could allow them to talk, we could break the influence of what Bacon called in *Novum Organum* 'the idols of the tribe', the man-centred nature of the man-made record, and would get to know much more about ourselves. While men have consistently claimed their superiority over the other animals because of our great 'rationality', it is more suitable to say that, of the pair of labour-dividers in the workplace, men and machines, the second are better suited to working in the idealized 'rational' mode than the first. Machines, therefore, of the pair, are the ones that men have groomed to be (merely) Mumford's Siemenses to his Faradays in his scheme for rationalizing the technical practice of an era that many call that of 'science-based technology'. And, if machines could talk they would doubtless admit that they like to work in this way, having been designed to do so. Man, in contrast, has continually fought to avoid getting involved personally in all those working tasks whose adoption would make him well-described as a 'rational' actor; 'rational' in the sense that a best solution is determined by the specification of working problems posed by others. Advisedly, too, for man prefers, in the main, to accept the challenge of having to use his judgement and imagination in face of the unknown for that is what he is particularly good at when lined up with the machines that he has made.[41]

To the extent, then, that there is any tendency, at any time, for there to be a genuine 'science base' to be built up for parts of the technical activity undertaken by men, so men will be inclined to invent a machine to take this over; for machines are good at doing what is explicable *ex ante* and is programmable. To the extent that there may be a real, rather than an imagined, tendency for technical change and inventive activity to stop being 'empirical' in type — and so no longer done in the trial-and-error mode that provides for man a special challenge — *homo faber* will see that he moves on. When the Faradays of the world are observed to be tugging at the strings of the Siemenses to tell them how to act, then is the time for man (and the Siemenses) to escape the embrace of 'technological revolution': something, which, in my judgement, he will always be able to avoid.[42] Try as the scientists may to get their dream-world of human rationality to come true and to be able to discern a genuine 'science-based technology', this will never happen, if only because of man's special relationship with his machines.

Is there any other reason to be so confident about this last issue, and about the assessment that the 'technology' construct has helped to make man seem machine-like in accounts set down about a phase after a 'technological revolution'? Human activity, as opposed to programmed- and machine-activity, is best described as being distinctively skilful; so it is too when compared with animal activity. Why there will never be a genuine 'technological revolution' in the technical arts and their products is really very simple. It is connected up with the propositions made before: the specialism of the scientist is best classed as an art and technical activity has always been primarily a trial-and-error affair, however much scientific knowledge has been available to the actor. The main factor influencing technical success is the skill of those doing the job and, in this respect, work dubbed 'technical' is not different from any other taken up by man, despite the mystification of a discussion about a 'science-link'. Machines have been made to fill the role of helping to allow *homo faber* to remain skilful at work; and this arrangement has been broadly successful over the years. Skill is acquired and improved while people are practising their specialism. So, because this practice of work cannot be accelerated greatly in the main, because skill cannot be acquired in a discontinuous way, and despite the notable existence of some one-off discontinuities in the form of inventions, technical change cannot be discontinuous across the board of human activity at any time. The key link with *homo faber*'s active and constructive skill makes it virtually certain that 'technological revolution' is only an artefact of the written record; it does not occur in the observable world that its discussants claim to be describing. Hence this idea is a distinctly-mythic, pre-Baconian construction, a creature of 'men's fancies'.[43]

V. Conclusion on 'Practice'

Present-day commentators can often be found to be talking in a kind of code when their subject matter of choice is human working activity of 'industrial' times. Thus, this kind of idea of 'technology', which was quoted in my paper on *Technik*, is often used or implied. It is widely held to be something like 'the systematic application of scientific or other organized knowledge to *practical* tasks'.[44] But what is this thing called 'practice' meant to be, given that commonsense allows scientists at work to 'apply' science to use, it making little sense to know them as 'technologists' for doing so? Physicists, cooks, wheelwrights and historians all 'practise' their specialist arts, skills and trades, no doubt. And people such as pianists and dancers often 'practise' privately nearly every day. What are the boundaries of this arena loosely known as 'practice' that allow technical work to be included, science as a process (the summertime one) normally to be excluded, and the so-called 'technology' to be dubbed an 'applied' sort of thing to be found doing?

The clue for solving this puzzle may be found with the comment previously quoted from Bacon about an inappropriate 'professorial style', with his contention that scientists could learn from the exercise of the crafts 'for they (as long as they are popular) seem full of life' and potentially successful, and with a proper grasp of the role of theory in human (as opposed to machine) working activity. For laymen have again followed the professors too blindly, this time into a jargon-filled world of 'unpopular' accounts of working practice which are scantily linked with the observation that the scientific record (springtime science) requires.

It is not that scientists and scholars make an explicit claim that 'theory' is the sole output of their work (and so the work of the 'practical' folk is thus downgraded), though theory is clearly a major part of this. And theory can be used in a general way to help order our perceptions about the world around us. Rather, all members of the tinkering species, *homo faber*, like to believe that they can discern order about them (except in the circumstances of those particular parts of the world that they themselves have designated to be 'problematical', and so worth their special attention, being disorderly in type). Thus a theory is an agreeable thing to voice if it has the result of rendering orderly the details of someone else's working patch, as with the

claims heard that 'technology' is (merely) 'practical' in type, being concerned with the 'application' of 'science' produced by others. And, in the
general scheme of the ordering of human working activity that is criticized
here — the one that casts into outer darkness, as being 'practical' in type,
some types of human work — the scientists and scholars seem to have classed
themselves, and their close associates, as 'theoretical' sorts of people, if only
because they cannot be called 'practical' sorts. Thus, they can seem to be
grander than those given the last label.

Although some scientists produce theories at work, or try to test other
people's theories,[45] it is not true of work in general that the actor (or,
perhaps, the 'participant' in work) starts from theory and then tries to
manipulate it in some way in order to make, or do, some other type of
product or service. Work, in general, is not well thought of as 'applying
knowledge', or 'applied theory', or 'applied science'. Indeed, if any general
pattern exists to link theory and human activity (or practice of specialist
arts) it is the opposite one. Theory stems from practice and is tested by it;
human working practice is typically mute and unprogrammable.[46]

It is because working problems have *not* yet been wrapped up and ordered
into theoretical and scientific statements articulated in books and articles
that they turn up as problems for actor-practitioners to try to solve. It is
because sufficient knowledge is *not* available to point to 'best solutions' to
problems posed in the working life that men are employed in those areas
and not machines. Given this, the 'applied science' idea, with which the
'technological revolution' construct is so closely associated, was always going
to be misleading and uninformative about human work. Given this, too,
any who have sought to argue that Francis Bacon's primary vision was that
of an 'industrial science' were always going to have trouble in understanding
his times and our own. To write in praise of a moveable feast called
'science' is to put icing on a cake of misconception.

It is, then, with a mis-assumption about the role of theory in work
generally that the constructors of the code-idea of a distinctive 'practice',
and 'practical' work, have seen fit to build up the new 'industrial philosophy'
of 'modern' times — a school of constructing records about working behaviour that neglects its main component, the personal skill of *homo faber*.
This is, perhaps, because human skill cannot readily be isolated, named and
observed in the manner of studying chemical substances. Take away any
two or three of the artefacts of the record for discussing the 'modern' world
and how it came about — craft, applied science, science as a process, industrial revolution, practical work, technological revolution, managerial revolution, science-based technology — and this whole scheme of dealing with
human achievement collapses in a heap of rubble. Use a simple Baconian
mode of inquiry, aiming to link abstractions set down on paper with observations of what can be seen, on what the scientists (the *Wissenschaftler*) say
about 'science' and you will find that academic referees are telling you that
the 'structure' of your work is terrible; your thinking is sloppy; your syntax
is appalling; your work is too discursive and is aiming at the wrong issue;
the issue, when it is distinguishable from the murk, is puerile; you should

have read Hogsnorton on Applied Hydronamic Processes; your work does not 'further our discipline'. All these criticisms may be true in part; but it is also true that those who let, in their discussion of 'technology', the notion of 'science' slip and slide about in the manner noted here are forging a 'model of the world in the understanding ... such as man's reason has distorted'.[47] Rossi's book on Bacon is sub-titled, 'From Magic to Science'; this paper might well be called, 'And Back to Magic Again', such is the amount of mysticism associated with the 'industrial science' idea.

Notes

1. Benjamin Farrington, *Francis Bacon: Philosopher of Industrial Science*, New York, 1949, p. 3.

2. J.D. Bernal, *Science in History*, London, 1954, p. 307; D.S.L. Cardwell, *Technology, Science and History*, London, 1972, p. 212; C.W. Pursell and M. Kranzberg, 'The Promise of Technology' in Kranzberg and Pursell (eds.), *Technology in Western Civilization*, New York, 1967, Vol. 2, p. 9. For a critique of Cardwell's scheme, see M. Fores, '*Technik*: or Mumford Reconsidered' in *History of Technology*, 6, 1981, pp. 122-6.

3. A.N. Whitehead, *Science and the Modern World*, Cambridge, 1926, Fontana paperback edition, pp. 120-1. My stress.

4. 'In the neotechnic phase, the main initiative comes not from the ingenious inventor, but from the scientist who establishes the general law: the invention is a derivative product.' Lewis Mumford, *Technics and Civilization*, London, 1934, p. 217.

5. Paolo Rossi, *Francis Bacon: From Magic to Science*, London, 1968; Margery Purver, *The Royal Society: Concept and Creation*, London, 1967, p. 35. Purver considers that this Society put 'into action' what was 'Bacon's plan for a scientific revolution'. *Ibid.*, p. 35.

6. Francis Bacon, *Novum Organum*, London, 1620, book 1, aphorism 124. On the general troubles that stem from latter-day misconception about the nature of science, see M. Fores, '*Homo Faber* and the American Disease' in *Cambridge Review*, XX, June 1982; 'Science and the Neolithic Paradox', typescript, 1982.

7. Whitehead, as note 3, pp. 13, 76.

8. Bacon, as note 6, preface.

9. See also M. Fores and A. Sorge, 'The Decline of the Management Ethic' in *Journal of General Management*, 6, Spring 1981; M. Fores, 'The Myth of a British Industrial Revolution' in *History*, 66, June 1981; Fores, as note 2; Fores, '*Homer Faber*', as note 6; A. Sorge and M. Fores, 'The Fifth Discontinuity', International Institute of Management, Berlin 1979, discussion paper: 79-84; Fores, 'Science', as note 6.

10. There are at least four conflicting uses of 'industry' in the literature. Fores, as note 9, p. 188.

11. Farrington, as note 1, p. 16.

12. See also Fores, as note 2.

13. See also M. Fores, '*Homo Faber* and the Articulation Trap', IIM, Berlin, 1981, mimeo.

14. Thus, too, the advice given to 'be rational' tends to mean 'do as I say' or 'agree with me'.

15. Whitehead, as note 3, p. 58. Bacon was trained as a lawyer at Cambridge and Gray's Inn, London.

16. Bacon, as note 6, book 2, aphorism 41.

17. M. Fores, 'The History of Technology: an Alternative View' in *Technology and Culture*, 20, October 1979.

18. Purver, as note 5, pp. 61, 42; Rossi, as note 5, p. 25.

19. Farrington, as note 1, p. 21.

20. *Ibid.*, p. 23.

21. Rossi, as note 5, p. 9.

22. *Ibid.*, p. 2.

23. Bacon, as note 6, book 1, aphorism 74. On the issue of 'modern'-day confusion about the links between 'theory' and working practice, see the last section of this paper and Sorge and Fores, as note 9.

24. For instance Whitehead, as note 3, pp. 58–61.

25. For instance Bernal, as note 2, p. 305.

26. See the passage, 'a story about science', in Fores, as note 2, pp. 130–4.

27. For instance Bryan Magee, *Popper*, London, 1973, chap. 2.

28. *Ibid.*, p. 43. The author's stress.

29. For more on scientific activity as an 'art', see Fores, as note 13.

30. Rossi, as note 5, pp. 10–11.

31. Francis Bacon, 'Catalogue of Particular Histories by Titles' in *The Works of Francis Bacon*, London, 1870, Vol. 4, p. 271.

32. See also M. Fores, 'Technical Change' in *Scandinavian Economic History Review*, forthcoming, 1982.

33. Jacob Schmookler, *Invention and Economic Growth*, Cambridge, Mass., 1966, p. 41.

34. For an attempt to integrate the treatment of design into that of 'technology', see Fores, as note 13.

35. Simon Kuznets, *Economic Growth and Structure*, London, 1966, p. 195; Mumford, as note 4, pp. 217–18; S Lilley, 'Technological Progress and the Industrial Revolution, 1700–1914' in Carlo M. Cipolla, ed., *Fontana Economic History of Europe*, Vol. 3, chap. 3, p. 60.

36. See also Fores and Sorge, as note 9; Fores, as note 13; Sorge and Fores, as note 9. In all these papers man is depicted as being characteristically a tinkerer as he goes about his work.

37. William N. Parker, 'Industry' in Peter Burke, ed., *The New Cambridge Modern History*, Vol. XIII, pp. 48, 51, 57. My stress.

38. This stems from the nature of (springtime) science as a form of public knowledge. See also the second section of this paper and Fores, 'Science', as note 6.

39. Human working behaviour is typically mute as men grapple to become familiar personally with the details facing them. For an amplification, see Sorge and Fores, as note 9.

40. For an expansion of this, see Fores, '*Homo Faber*', as note 6.

41. Much the same argument can be applied to the arena called 'management' by English speakers. Fores and Sorge, as note 9.

42. The so-called 'new information technology' does not appear to be producing a 'technological revolution' either. A. Sorge *et al.*, 'Microelectronics and Manpower in Manufacturing', IIM, Berlin, 1981, discussion paper: LMP 81–16.

43. On skill as an individual possession, see also the paper on the American Disease, as note 6.

44. Fores, '*Technik*', as note 2, p. 124.

45. A criticism of Popper's work, besides that outlined earlier here, is that it is

overconcerned with the grand and the dramatic in scientific inquiry: the generation of prominent theories.

46. A. Sorge and G. Hartmann, 'Technology and Labour Markets', IIM, Berlin, 1980, discussion paper: 80–9; A. Sorge, 'Cultured Organization', IIM, Berlin, 1980: IIM paper 80–9; Sorge and Fores, as note 9.

47. 'The idols of the tribe are inherent in human nature . . .; for man's sense is falsely asserted to be the standard of things; on the contrary, all the perceptions both of the senses and the mind bear reference to man and not to the universe, and the human mind resembles those uneven mirrors which impart their own properties to different objects, from which rays are emitted and distort and disfigure them.' Bacon, as note 6, book 1, aphorism 41.

The Purpose and Principles of Research in an Electrical Manufacturing Business of Moderate Size, as Stated by J. A. Crabtree in 1930

EDITED AND INTRODUCED BY D. G. TUCKER

The study of the origins of industrial research has attracted a good deal of interest among historians of technology in recent years, especially in the United States. In the electrical industry, research in the form of experiments conducted more or less scientifically was implicit from the beginnings of the industry in the second half of the nineteenth century, but did not become explicit (for example in the form of a 'research department' or 'research laboratory') until the early years of the twentieth century — in Britain not until after the First World War.[1] Once the era of industrial research in electrical engineering in Britain had really begun in the 1920s, there were numerous papers published on how it should be organized and what its purpose was.[2] These papers were concerned with the research departments of large industrial or government organizations. Research was hardly associated with manufacturing firms of, say, 1,000 employees or less. It is therefore very refreshing to come across a down-to-earth treatment of the purpose, nature and organization of industrial research, written in 1930 by the founder and proprietor of a firm manufacturing small electrical switches and accessories with a workforce not exceeding 1,000 up to that time. The document concerned was never published and seems now to be of considerable historical importance in showing the thinking of a successful manufacturer who apparently had no ambition to be a tycoon, only to remain successful. It forms the subject of this article.

After the introductory sections, this article comprises an abridgement of two chapters in what was clearly intended to be a comprehensive textbook of business management prepared half a century ago. Its author was John Ashworth Crabtree who, starting from very small beginnings, founded in 1919 the well-known manufacturing business still known by his name and still based in Walsall, West Midlands. The firm was successful and expanded greatly both during and after Crabtree's lifetime, but he unfortunately died in 1935 at the rather early age of 49. The proposed book was drafted in 1930 and remained as an unrevised typescript,[3] probably forgotten, until recently brought to my notice by Crabtree's eldest son, Mr Jack Crabtree.

The reason why the work was never revised and published is not now known. It was a long work, setting out Crabtree's views of the principles by which a manufacturing business should be run, based largely on his own experience of running his own firm, which by 1930 had about 1,000 employees, and also partly on his observations and studies of bigger firms. It was in many respects a pioneering work, for the principles of business management, however well understood intuitively by businessmen, had not then been subject to much explicit analysis.[4]

The two chapters dealing with research are particularly interesting to historians of technology and to engineers, firstly because research was not then (or now!) a particularly noticeable feature of most small and medium-sized firms,[5] and secondly because the ideas put forward still seem as valid as ever. In this article I have made a précis of Crabtree's text, of about 40 per cent of the length of the original, using entirely Crabtree's own words and method of presentation, merely omitting what seemed to me the less valuable portions. I believe I have retained entirely the spirit of the original.

Some Comments on Crabtree's Analysis

It has for long been customary to discuss the subject of the inter-relationships between science, technology, research, industry, business and society in abstruse, tortuous and convoluted terms. Crabtree approaches his admittedly more limited analysis in a direct, penetrating and lucid manner. It was perhaps this which led one of my colleagues, a man with good experience of modern industrial research in electrical engineering, to describe Crabtree's approach as 'naive'. My own forty years' experience of applied research in electrical engineering has been in government and academic departments where the constraints and interacting factors are rather different from those in industry. I am therefore not too well qualified to express an opinion, but I would have thought Crabtree was very far from being naive. Talking of product development towards the end of these chapters on research, Crabtree says: 'The best and most reliable product is ever that which fulfils its function with the minimum of complication and the maximum of simplicity.' Is not his analysis of industrial research itself just an example of his putting his principles into practice?

It is interesting that while Crabtree sees research as having a fundamental role in progressive and competitive industry, he also implies that research is not so much a means of attaining profitability *per se* as rather a means of ensuring survival, of maintaining a market lead by offering a better product than one's competitors; it is interesting that he never mentions the idea of research leading to a *cheaper* product. (Traditionally the Crabtree firm has made only better-quality products.)[6]

Crabtree's view that perfection means stagnation — the time to get out a new product — is interesting and probably now widely accepted; and with his principle that compromise in design is essential, his definition of perfection is obviously relative rather than absolute.

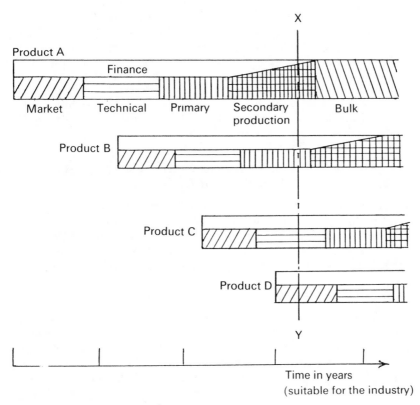

Figure 1. The ideal state of balanced research as applied to separate products, groups of products or departments. (As given by Crabtree)

It is not only technical research that he sees as important; all aspects of the business are to be appraised in a scientific fashion. The work is to be programmed as shown in Fig. 1 so that a proper balance is obtained. It is believed he put all his principles into practice.

One last point: Crabtree saw clearly the distinction between industrial and basic research: 'We must be able to distinguish between research which a business is justified in making and the more specialised research which is the work of a university or specialist laboratory.' It is interesting that many *large* industrial organizations in many countries, including Britain, began around Crabtree's time to engage in basic scientific research. What was the justification and reason for this? In her examination of the history of research in the Bell Telephone System,[7] Lillian Hoddeson poses but leaves unanswered this intriguing question. Could the answer lie in the increasing isolation of the research department in an ever-expanding large firm from the business and manufacturing sides, which permitted the realization of the natural desire of the academically-trained staff to pursue more academic research?[8] In a firm of the size of Crabtree's this could not apply and he did not see it as a permissible development. He saw research as an integrated activity over the whole field of business operations from market research to production research, from finance to science and technology. There was (and is) obviously no place for research without direct relevance in the activities of a small or medium-sized firm; yet in a huge organization like Bell, with ample resources, it could have the most profound influence on the course of technology — for example, the transistor.

Abridged Transcription of Crabtree's Views of the Principles of Research

It does not seem to be possible in these days to maintain a business on an even, undisturbed level of steady, profitable turnover. It seems as though the business must either progress, or decline, with no possibility of balance between. Any such state of balance seems so limited and precarious as to be practically non-existent, and it is preferable to ignore its remote possibility.

There is no static condition in a business: it must either progress or decline

The period of decline may be long drawn out. Indeed, I have often been surprised at the time an old-established business can linger in spite of mismanagement. Occasionally, when the whole industry is expanding, one will find that the natural growth of the market will carry the business long enough to enable new men to grow up into control, and who will then revivify the organization with new creative thought. With an intensive market, however, the decline is more rapid and, at times, spectacular.

The progress of a business in any competitive market is largely dependent upon the creative effort put into its products and management, and it is in this effort that the scientific methods of research can be so valuable.

Research plus creative thought and decision constitutes the soundest foundation for business progress

I understand by research that systematic, scientific enquiry into our problems by careful experimentation, wherever possible; a clear distinction between those things which are facts, and those things which are approximations, and finally an accurate analysis as to the significance to be attached to the various facts, the approximations and the unknowns, which make up the 'formulae' of our knowledge. I find that it is becoming increasingly difficult to know one's facts, and thereby to make correct decisions. I see no other way of meeting this difficulty save on the basis, that to every problem in commerce and industry, the systematic methods of scientific analysis, research and experiment, will indicate some solution.

Research should not lessen our creative effort, for it does not offer a 'Royal Road to Success'. But it does help to indicate the way, saving the waste of our energy in a maze of wavering impulses — and helps us in the final decisions, by ensuring that they have a definite bias to progress.

This conception of research has the widest possible application to our business experience. It involves something much wider than the old idea, so popularized by our advertising friends, of the scientist holding up a test tube to the light, or peering into a microscope. It would be true to say that —

Systematic research will suggest a solution to every business problem

Once this principle is accepted, our mental attitude to our business becomes reorientated. We are no longer content with 'snap' decisions based upon insufficient facts, and we prefer to take action slowly, confident of the surety of our ultimate steps. There are times when, in consequence of this slower but surer attitude, we may seem to lag behind our more spectacular competitors; but the greater ultimate progress must go inevitably to the business whose fundamental research is the surer, and whose research work is untiringly persistent.

Research has its promise in every phase of our business; policy, finance, organization, management, service, product, production, and the rest. There is no field of business activity where research cannot help.

I have found that industries as a whole may be divided into two distinct groups:

(1) Those industries in which research is rare and progress has been extremely slow, with products and practice changing very little.
(2) Those industries in which research is continually operating to render products and practice obsolete.

The distinction is not necessarily inherent in an industry, but seems — so far as one can judge it from British conditions — to be due to the traditional type of mind in each specific industry. The first type of mind is indicated in agriculture and certain branches of the iron and steel trades, where it is still possible to obtain a bare and precarious living by the methods of the Victorian era, with the result that many men and methods operate much as they did fifty years ago.

A typical industry of the second class is the motor industry — an industry which has had such remarkable changes and developments during the last ten years that changes in design have almost become a fetish of the industry. Firms will bring out new models which are often no better than their predecessors, having only the virtue of being different. This fetish of 'change' has indeed become such a curse to certain firms in the motor industry, that unless it can be checked, it will eventually mean the extinction of that particular organization.

Where an industry changes little — being largely dependent upon tradition — we find that research, carefully planned and adapted, tends to produce very beneficial results, in comparison with the effort necessary. Where, however, an industry is based upon continual research as is now becoming universal, the competition in research itself tends to lessen the commercial return upon any invention or development. This comes about in two ways.

In the first place, should you initiate any new development, which may have taken years in its conception, it will at once be attacked by your competitors. They see at once how *you* have solved the problem, and they immediately receive the free benefit of much of your research. They start — not where you started — but helped considerably by what they see you have rejected, and the usual result is that their trouble and research are halved. I have found that whenever we break new ground in design, it takes the trade half the time to produce their alternative product to compete that it took us in research and experiment to produce our own. It is not long after the introduction of the competitive product that the resultant price war renders our own product unremunerative, and have come to accept as a principle that —

A product is profitable after marketing for much less than the time it took in research

The proportion must obviously vary according to the type of product, but the ratio will be well below 100 per cent. There is a reason why this should be so. Immediately your idea is known, you disclose how the problem has been solved by yourself. Much of the original work in research is in exploring how the problem should be attacked. Your solution, as exemplified by your product, shows how you have solved this, and your competitor's problem is reduced very considerably by this solution.

Some years ago we decided to re-design an electrical product having a wood case enclosing a porcelain interior to carry the mechanism. We wished to use a synthetic resin case, and decided that we must forget the traditions of design involved in the wood and porcelain product and discover new principles of design based upon the new material. It took us two years to decide these principles, and a further two years to apply them to the product. Meanwhile, our competitors merely tackled the problem by making the original wood case of synthetic resin and retaining the traditional interior of a porcelain mounted mechanism. Immediately our own product was marketed, the work of our first two years was at once apparent. Anyone could see how we had faced the problem and solved it on different principles of approach. The research problem of our competitors was accordingly halved and within two years the majority had been able to re-design and market their products.

This is a simple example of what I have seen happen very many times in my experience, and it emphasizes the need to express the result of our research with rigour, immediately it can be commercialized. 'Facile est inventis addere' is a highly effective restriction upon the profitability of research in modern industry.

A product becomes unprofitable and obsolete as it approaches perfection

I have found that as a product, a method or a service becomes so nearly perfect that it is almost impossible to improve it further, it is, in fact, obsolete and out of date. Eventually there comes a time when everything has been done which can be done within the basic limitations of design inherent within the specific product. When there is nothing left to improve — and within its basic limitations the product is therefore nearly perfect — it is necessary to recognize that it is obsolete, and a new aspect of research must be initiated. We have now to go back to first principles, create new basic limitations to design and produce an entirely new product.

Essentials of research policy

It is not enough to limit our conception of research to the technical or chemical laboratory, but rather to view research as having the widest applicability to all our problems in business and higher control. I therefore state the essentials of research to the business as a whole, considering research as having the widest application possible. We have as our first consideration —

Essential 1: Balance

The first essential is that the whole of the research activities of the business shall be balanced — that research in any one department shall not be pursued at the expense of others.

To give an idea of the research necessary in any business, I would mention (1) Organization and administration, (2) Finance, (3) Production (Machines and Processes), (4) Technical (Product and Service), (5) Markets and (6) Human Element or Personnel. These are six main divisions in which research should be continually pursued and in which the work being done should be balanced. Figure 1 shows in conventional form (the time elements in fact being variable) what I consider to be the ideal state in our own business of balanced research directed to the production of some new product.

From the original decision to investigate the possibilities of the product to its ultimate production, there are (in our case) six stages, some of which may operate in succession or be contemporary.

(1) Market research.
(2) Laboratory and technical research.
(3) Finance (involving costs).
(4) Primary (or experimental) production or development.
(5) Secondary (or small quantity) production or development, being the first factory stage.
(6) Bulk (or standard) production being the final factory stage.

When you arrive at bulk production the product merges into the general output of your business.

I do not like to start more than one major line of research at one time. With that well started and in operation, we can then give attention to a second line of research, but not before. The same principle can apply to those working out the detailed work of research, with the result that if you consider the line X, Y (Fig. 1) cutting through the major section of research, it gives a cross section of the ideal research activities of the business at any moment.

We should have at any one moment:[9]

One line of market research.
One line of technical research.
One line of primary production research.
One line of secondary production research.
One line of bulk production research.

And finally the research essential to production as spread over the various products or departments concerned.

This diagram (Fig. 1) is only symbolical. It suggests a balance of research which is the ideal to be aimed at. Its characteristics will vary according to the specific business under consideration.

In a large business the principle of balance would still hold good, but the emphasis on individual research would require further subdivision. The whole of such research would demand a distinct executive control. If the balance is to be maintained by the man responsible for such control, he must not be unduly influenced by his own specific type of scientific training. He should be an organizer trained to think scientifically, and not a scientist trying to organize.

Essential 2: Compromise

The great distinction between research in its purely scientific form and research in a business lies in the fact that successful business research aims at compromise. To give a technical illustration: we have one mechanism to make, of which the working part goes into about one-eighth of a cubic inch. Within that volume we have to produce a mechanism which will work about a million times without re-oiling; it has to have mechanical strength, electrical insulation, has to break an electric arc and to carry an electric current. There is no way of making a mechanism ensuring all these essentials in completeness, for there is a limit to all material things. Thus we are driven to realize that our essential aim is one of compromise. If you make one feature better than another, it is definitely at the expense of some other feature, and I am amused when any of my competitors emphasize one technical point and ignore the others, for it is impossible to obtain a high degree of perfection in any single unit of development, without paying on the debit side in some other essential factor. This compromise in the application of research applies not only to materials, design, manufacture, and organization, but also in the less tangible problems of finance, market research and personnel.

Essential 3: The long view

It is essential in any research that we maintain a long view with regard to our problem. We are today reaping in commercial results what was sown in past research, and the research of today is the sowing for the business harvest in the coming years. For that reason our research requires planning, to form part of an unending process of enquiry into the needs of our business. We must, however, retain a correct perspective of the function of research in business, and recognize that there are limits to what we can afford to do.

We must, for example, be able to distinguish between research which a business is justified in making and the more specialized research which is the work of a university or specialist laboratory.

Essential 4: Honesty to face the facts

It is a basic essential that in our research we must face our problems free from bias and with open minds. If we, as the head executives of a business, controlling the research work of certain assistants, are but desirous of confirming our 'guesses' our staffs will quickly learn that we do not require the truth from them, but only some confirmation of our own ideas. They will soon colour their facts, to harmonize with what they think we want. If such an attitude becomes general among those carrying out our research work, then the time and money spent is an absolute waste and a drain in the business, for it ceases to be research.

Knowing when you have got what you require

[This stage of research] is more commercial and materialistic: to recognize when you have got what you want and apply it. Many firms waste a great deal of time in going beyond what is sufficient for the commercial needs of the moment. There is a relation between the prospective volume of profits and the cost of investigation; and that the principle of diminishing returns shows the inadvisability of working too long on one problem. It is better to spread or rotate studies, covering all matters that offer a reasonable chance of profitable improvement.

As to when we have gone far enough, I find this question helps most: 'Is the solution simple?' If it is not simple and direct in comparison with present practice and knowledge, it is not enough and we must continue our work. When we have obtained simplicity, the time is due for its introduction to practice. This is not to suggest that simplicity in fact, or form, or design is easy or accidental. The opposite is usually true. Whenever I see a product which is extremely simple, I always feel that an enormous amount of thought has gone into that product. Nothing is ever reduced to simplicity except by an enormous effort in thought and experiment. The best and most reliable product is ever that which fulfils its function with the minimum of complication and the maximum of simplicity. It is to the degree that we attain this, that we decide when to apply the results of our research in actual practice.

The conclusion of research with a view to decision and action

All business research is unremunerative unless it is given expression in some productive activity. The final stage is therefore the decision and action by the higher control, who direct the conclusion of the research worker into business activity. This stage may in fact be the greatest stage of all, for it involves the whole field of development, wherein the conclusions of research are applied to actual practice. In some cases development may have been contemporary to research. In others it will be subsequent.

Notes

1. An excellent account of the development of research in the Bell Telephone organization is given by L. Hoddeson, 'The emergence of basic research in the Bell Telephone System, 1875–1915' in *Technology and Culture*, 22, 1981, pp. 512–44. Hoddeson shows that the Bell company started employing people with a specific commitment to experimentation and invention from 1878, although the numbers were very small (single figures) until 1911, when a 'research branch' was set up which had twenty members by 1912 and expanded explosively thereafter. In Britain, the Post Office, which had rather wider operating responsibilities than the Bell system but little manufacturing activity, had shown concern with experimentation and novel design ever since the nationalization of the telegraphs in 1870, and when W. H. Preece became electrician to the Post Office in 1877 he was able to assign staff to experimental work. A great deal of fundamental engineering research and development (but not basic physics) was done by Post Office staff before the First World War, but there was no formal research organization until after that war. See early volumes of *P.O. Elect. Engrs. J.* (which started in 1907) and D. G. Tucker, 'The early development of the British underground trunk telephone network' in *Trans. Newcomen Soc.*, 49, 1977–8, pp. 57–74, and 'Sir William Preece (1834–1913)', *ibid.*, 53, 1981–2, in course of publication (read to Society on 10 March 1982; preprints available). On the heavier side of electrical engineering in Britain, the electricity supply industry also developed without the benefit of formal research organizations until after the First World War, when some of the big manufacturing firms such as Metropolitan-Vickers and British Thomson-Houston set up research departments, and the British Electrical and Allied Industries Research Association (ERA) was formed (in 1920). In the earlier years, consulting electrical engineers such as John Hopkinson and Gisbert Kapp had played a leading role in experimentation and novel design, along with the outstandingly innovative industrialists such as S. Z. de Ferranti and R. E. B. Crompton. See J. Greig, *John Hopkinson*, Science Museum, London, 1970; D. G. Tucker, *Gisbert Kapp*, Univ. of Birmingham, 1973; A. Ridding, *S. Z. de Ferranti*, Science Museum, London, 1964; B. Bowers, *R. E. B. Crompton*, Science Museum, London, 1969.

2. Two papers, in particular, are worth referring to here. The earlier one was A. P. M. Fleming, 'Planning a works research organization' in *J. Inst. Elect. Engrs.*, 57, 1919, pp. 153–70, discussion pp. 170–92. (This was later expanded into a book, A. P. M. Fleming and J. G. Pearce, *Research in Industry*, Pitman, London, 1922.) The later one was W. Wilson, 'Industrial research, with special reference to electrical engineering development' in *J.I.E.E.*, 62, 1923–4, pp. 61–82, discussion pp. 83–107. The lengthy discussions and very full bibliographies show how great an interest had been aroused in the question of industrial research at this time.

3. An original carbon copy is now in the Archives of the Institution of Electrical Engineers at Savoy Place, London, WC2R 0BL, kindly deposited by Crabtree's son, Mr Jack Crabtree, who was Chairman of the firm for many years until his recent retirement.

4. The contribution made by Crabtree's work is discussed in A. L. Minkes and D. G. Tucker, 'J. A. Crabtree: a pioneer of business management' in *Business History*, 21, 1979, pp. 198–212.

5. Some twenty years ago, Mr John Hudson of the University of Birmingham made, at my request, some inquiries into the extent of research and innovation in electrical manufacturing firms in the West Midlands of size between about 200 and 2,000 employees. In spite of letters and personal visits to senior members of staff and directors, it proved impossible to obtain really meaningful information. It was clear,

however, that research in any accepted sense was absent from most firms, although in contrast there were one or two where as much as 0.5 to 1 per cent of the employees might be engaged in investigative or innovative work which could sometimes lead to patentable inventions. One firm had a disproportionately large research effort because it had been awarded 'cost-plus' government research contracts — a form of work (so often cost-ineffective) that would have been unknown to Crabtree.

6. The role of research in increasing profits was expressed bluntly by A. P. M. Fleming (paper cited in note 2): 'It is an economic error to assume that the best method of increasing profits is, through trade combinations or other means of protection, to increase selling price. A much more logical method is to bring about the difference between manufacturing cost and selling price by reducing the cost of manufacture, and it is in this connection that the possibilities of research are unlimited.' On the other hand, in his book (see also note 2) he recognizes the survival element (p. 39): '... research is an insurance in which a suitable proportion of immediate returns is spent to secure the continuance of the returns in future.'

7. Cited in note 1.

8. As early as 1919, C. C. Paterson (who became Director of the GEC research laboratories) said: '... a great deal of latitude ought to be allowed to a research worker if he seems sometimes to deviate from the rigid industrial path. Apart from other considerations, there must be in a research laboratory a real spirit of research, and one cannot foster this by constant limitations.' (Discussion on paper by Fleming, see note 2.)

9. I have taken the liberty of correcting what must have been errors in Crabtree's typescript; he had 'major', 'experienced' and 'primary' where I have put 'market', 'primary' and 'secondary', respectively.

Ancient Mortars and Concretes: Aspects of their Durability

ROMAN MALINOWSKI

Introduction

Mortars and concretes of unusual durability have been discovered in the remains of many remarkable ancient buildings and engineering structures.[1] Despite centuries of use and exposure to adverse environmental conditions, these mortars and concretes have often survived better than the natural stone or burnt brick found in the same structures and sometimes even better than modern concretes exposed to similar conditions.[2]

This paper combines the author's previously presented investigations [3, 4] with the results of new tests and some consideration of the procedures discussed in the classical literature. Examples are presented of structures and material which display excellent durability. Studies *in situ* have been complemented with laboratory tests in which physical and mechanical properties, the microstructure and the chemical composition of the material were analysed. From these enquiries it has been possible to attempt an explanation of why these ancient materials are so durable and to comment on the methods used in their original application. Finally attention is drawn to problems which remain and whose clarification would be useful.

Durable Lime Mortars

The protection of a weaker substratum of walls, columns and floors by careful polishing of fresh lime mortar has its origins in early antiquity. The first known use of this procedure is to be found on the Mask of Jericho of 7000 B.C.[5] (see Fig. 1). Later on many examples of high-quality polished mortar have been confirmed in, for example, Mycenaean and Minoan settlements (1500 B.C.), in the famous cistern of Mycenae, and in many buildings of Phaestos (Fig. 2) and Malia in Crete. The Greeks took over this ancient technique and subsequently the Romans applied it to hydraulic structures. Floors, walls and columns in cisterns and the interior of aqueducts were covered with a single or multiple layer of finely polished mortar. Examples of the use of a single layer are the Greek cistern at Megara (500 B.C.) and the Roman aqueduct bridge, the Pont du Gard (*c.* 15 B.C.). Multiple layers were used in the cisterns of King Solomon and the Herodian aqueduct at Caesarea (early first century).[2, 4] Vitruvius (Bk. VII, Ch. III) describes the polishing of mortars as an old Greek technique. He states that careful polishing helps to restrain shrinkage and cracking. Vitruvius also

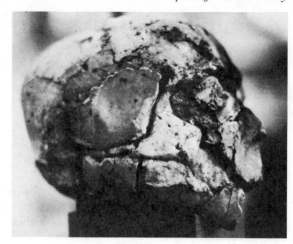

Figure 1. The Mask of Jericho. The skull covered with polished mortar-plaster (centre), 7000 B.C. By courtesy of the Museum of Rockefeller, Jerusalem.

discusses the roles of the various components of mortars laid up from three or six layers.

The explanation of the mechanism and function of the polishing technique of mortar, as well as the function of the multiple thin layers, is the result of recent studies.[2, 3, 4]

The polishing, being essentially a process which grinds the lime, carbonate or pozzolana of the mortar, creates a dense capillary structure at the surface which increases the impermeability of the material. The carbonation and hydration (that is, the hardening) are also accelerated and the strength and durability improved. It is supposed that the finely polished, hardened surface not only restrains shrinkage and cracking but also inhibits the formation of lime sediments on the walls of cistern and aqueducts due to a better flow of water. The removal of such sediments during maintenance work is also easier.[6]

Studies have also been made of the composition and function of the multiple six-layer mortar on the Caesarean aqueduct.[2, 3] These thin layers of the mortar, each placed and finished separately (after short pauses which are needed for some hardening), cause a uniaxial, normally directed shrinkage, thus restraining horizontal cracking. The lightweight greyish layer containing cool ashes is a bond layer; the white, carbonated layer containing marble powder prevents shrinkage; and the reddish, very fine polished pozzolanic layer (of ground ceramic) assures hardening in water, impermeability and strength (Figs 3 and 4). Lightweight lava aggregate was often used in mortars. Specimens have been found in the buildings of the Forum Romanum in Ostia, in Pompeii and Herculanum. The great permanence of such polished mortars is explained by the low water absorption and the desorbtion of the aggregate which, acting in a similar fashion to entruded air, affects the swelling and shrinkage of the mortar.

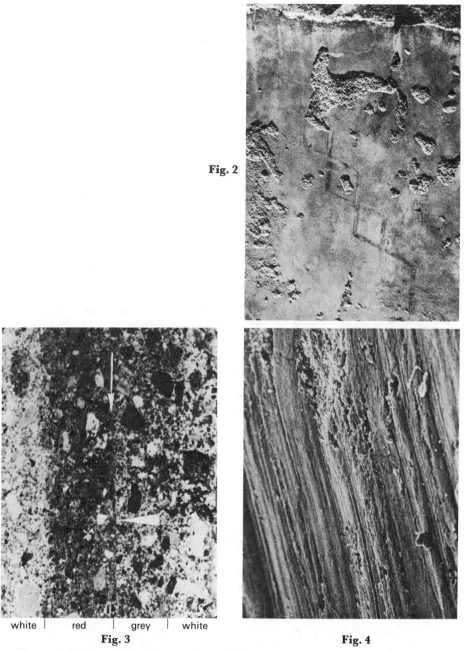

Fig. 2

white | red | grey | white
Fig. 3   **Fig. 4**

Figure 2. Painted wall in Phaestos, Crete, 1500 B.C.
Figure 3. Section of the multilayer mortar in the aqueduct lining of Caesarea, A.D. 0–50. Section, magnification × 3.
Figure 4. SEM micrograph of a polished surface of the red mortar. Detail marked in Fig. 3. Magnification × 400.

Durable Structural Concrete

Concrete, *opus caementitium*, is generally supposed to be a material of Roman origin. However, the use of mortar and plaster in Greek buildings — which is described in detail by Vitruvius in Book VII — suggests that concrete was in all probability used in the pre-Roman period. This view is borne out by studies of the cistern at Kameiros in Rhodes (500 B.C.) whose walls are covered in pozzolanic concrete (Figs 5 and 6).

For structures built under water or in which concrete of great strength and durability was necessary — for example in protecting walls, harbours, aqueducts and buildings in very cold climates — a lime-pozzolana binder was often used. The use of this type of concrete has been confirmed in the harbours of Ostia, Puteoli and Villa Polia (near Sorrento) and in many buildings of the Capitolium. Especially interesting is the town wall of Ampurias in Spain (A.D. 50). It is made of lime-pozzolana concrete and was built without any dilatation. Not a single crack is visible in the hundreds of metres of the wall which survive (Fig. 7).

It should not be concluded that a lime-pozzolana binder was *always* resorted to for the more important Roman constructions.[2, 7] There were exceptions. Sometimes, even in hydraulic and marine structures and at mineral springs, lime-based concrete was often used and expected to meet the needs of long-term durability. Examples are the north German aqueducts at Eifel and other places.[8]

In both lime and pozzolana-lime (Fig. 8) concretes, differing types of coarse aggregates were utilized. Various natural gravels, crushed aggregates of heavy basalt of porphyry, granite or limestone, and crushed clay bricks, tiles and light lava were all used. In one case gap grade aggregate concrete has been discovered. Vitruvius (Bk II, Ch. IV) describes in detail sands of different qualities and recommends their various applications. The lime/sand ratio was adjusted to the quality of the sand (Figs 9, 10, 11).

To improve primarily the durability of concrete, but also its workability, air entrainment was applied to concrete exposed to frost action (Fig. 12). This has been revealed by the very interesting microscopical investigations of Idorn.[9] Lightweight concrete made of lava aggregate was often used in Roman buildings to provide better insulation and to reduce weight. A famous example is the top part of the dome of the Pantheon (Fig. 13).

In *De Architectura*, Vitruvius recommends various rules for the selection, proportioning, mixing and compaction of concrete. It is interesting therefore to observe that the concretes used in many structures from different parts of the Roman Empire do indeed display evidence that these rules were observed. The examples of crackless structure in many Roman buildings indicate a proper choice and adjustment of the material and a sound understanding of the material's behaviour when applied to different structural forms in varying environmental conditions. This is exemplified by, for example, thick concrete sloping walls and domes and arches cast in massive concrete such as the Pantheon and the Basilicae of Constantine and Maxentius. The curvature of these structures results in uniaxial vertical creep

Figure 5. Concrete walls of the cistern of Kameiros, Rhodes, *c.* 500 B.C.[4]
Figure 6. Section of concrete from the cistern of Kameiros. Detail of Fig. 5 (1:2).
Figure 7. The town wall of Ampurias, Spain, A.D. 0–50.
Figure 8. Example of lime-silica reaction in ancient concrete (harbour of Caesarea).
Magnification × 92. (Malinowski *et al.*, 1961)[2]

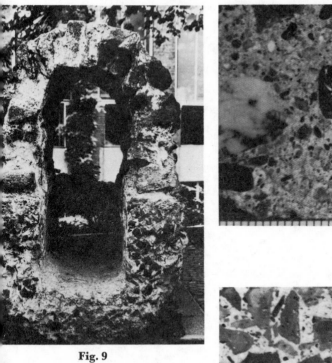

Fig. 9

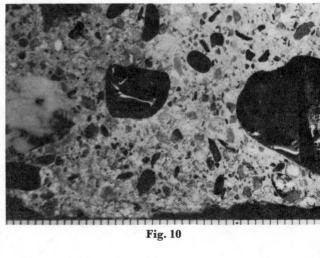

Fig. 10

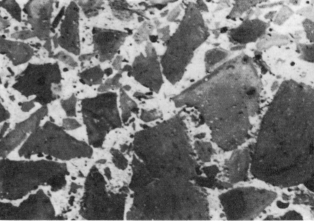

Fig. 11

Figure 9. Basaltic aggregate concrete of the Eifel aqueduct, Cologne, West Germany (A.D. 100).

Figure 10. Gravel concrete of the pavement substrate, Italica, Spain (A.D. 150). Magnification × 2.

Figure 11. Crushed brick-gap grade, Trier, West Germany (A.D. 200). Magnification × 0.7.

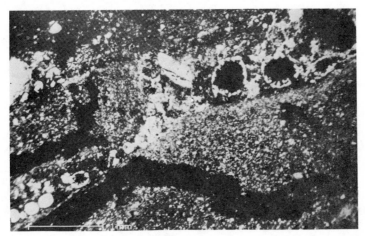

Figure 12. Air-entrained concrete, Barbegal aqueduct, Provence, A.D. 0–100 (Idorn, 1959).[9] Magnification × 35.

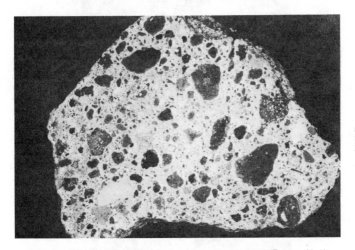

Figure 13. Lightweight lava aggregate concrete, Rome (1:1).

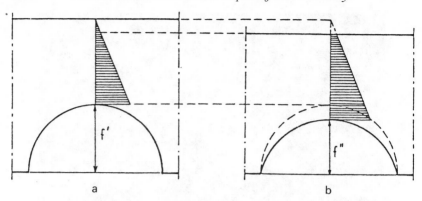

Figure 14. Diagram of pressure and deformation in an arch: (a) at early age; (b) after long time loading. (Malinowski, 1979.[3])

Figure 15. *Opus insertum* of gypsum concrete in the harbour walls of Kition, 600 B.C. (?).

deformation of the concrete and restrained creep in the horizontal direction which compensates for the shrinkage deformation and avoids cracking (Fig. 14).[3]

Special Solutions

Occasionally ancient builders adopted particularly unusual and interesting solutions to problems of materials.The type of gypsum concrete used as a binder in the Pyramids has also been found in the walls of the Palace of Mycenae and as a cement between giant blocks of the ancient harbour of Kition in Cyprus (600 B.C.?). This rare example of the durability of gypsum concrete in a marine structure would repay further study (Fig. 15).

Another interesting technique is the use of an expanding paste for fitting the joints of pipes in pressurized pipe-lines. The paste, which was first found in Knossos,[10] has subsequently been identified in many Greek and Roman pipes made of lead, clay and stone. The pipe-joints sealed in this way ensured that internal pressures equivalent to many atmospheres could be-safely sustained. In the famous Pergamon aqueduct (Figs 16 and 17) the

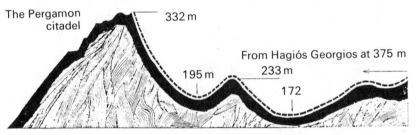

Figure 16. The lead aqueduct of the citadel of Pergamon, 200 B.C. (by courtesy of G. Sandstrom).[12]

Figure 17. The lead pipe sealed in a stone block head, Ephesos, 200 B.C. (Fahlbusch - Malinowski, 1981.)[6]

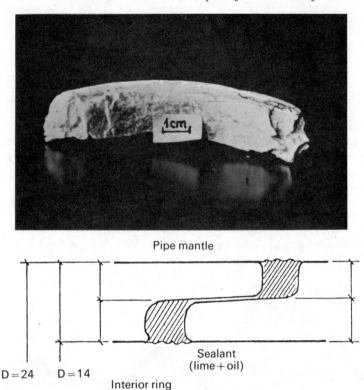

Pipe mantle

D = 24   D = 14

Interior ring

Sealant
(lime + oil)

Figure 18. The sealing paste from a clay pressure pipe, Rhodes, 500 B.C.

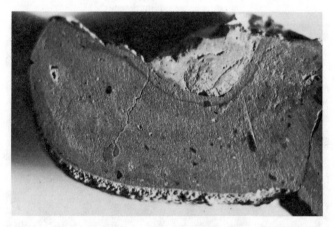

Figure 19. Traces of a penetrated fluid (probably oil) in the clay pipe at the boundary with the jointing paste.

lead pipes were subjected to a pressure of nearly 20 atmospheres. The sealing material used in this case was the one described by Vitruvius (Bk VIII, Ch. VI), a mixture of quicklime and oil to which was probably added finely ground limestone, as in Vitruvian stucco mortar. This formula was confirmed in tests carried out by the author (Figs 18 and 19).[3, 6] A similar paste has been found also in the mosaic floors of Roman baths where the functions of sealant and water-repellent were alike. Another material for sealing water-pipe joints by expansion, montmorillonite, was found in one of the Pergamon aqueducts.[11] In low-pressure aqueducts the pipes were often embedded in concrete (Fig. 20).[12]

Figure 20. Pressure conduit embedded in concrete, Caesarea, Israel, A.D. 0–50.

Stone beams reinforced with iron bars have been found at Propylaia.[13] How such reinforcing bars were protected against corrosion is not known. To ensure the durability of floors exposed to frost action, Vitruvius (Bk VII, Ch. 1) suggests impregnating the mortar jointing between the stone flags with oil. A similar technique is used today for pavements in the United States.

Conclusions

This paper has described briefly a number of impressive and successful building techniques used by ancient engineers: single and multiple layered mortars; surface polishing techniques to protect weaker internal layers; various concretes based on different binders and aggregates; air entrainment to improve durability; the impregnation of jointing materials with oil; expanding water-pipe sealants. Studies of these techniques reveal that ancient engineers had a sound understanding of numerous aspects of the construction, protection and maintenance of engineering structures and components.

In the ancient world a lack of scientific method and specialized knowledge were compensated by experience based on traditional practices and know-how of a more general character. In modern times, invention and engineering solutions frequently precede a full scientific explanation. Ancient engineering techniques were used for centuries in the absence of a clear scientific understanding of what was involved. Nevertheless, what was done was eminently successful; what was achieved could be very impressive indeed. Many of the techniques and processes evolved are of interest — and sometimes importance — to modern concrete engineers, historians of science and technology and archaeologists.

Acknowledgments

I would like to thank all who have helped in the preparation of this paper and especially Dr N.A.F. Smith, Dr G.M. Idorn, Miss B. Lendheim and my wife Maria.

Notes

1. N. Davey, *A History of Building Materials*, Phoenix House, London, 1961.

2. R. Malinowski *et al.*, 'Durability of Roman Mortars and Concretes' in *RILEM*, Prague, 1961.

3. R. Malinowski, 'Concretes and Mortars in Ancient Aqueducts' in *Concrete International*, Vol. 1, No. 1, 1979, pp. 66–76.

4. R. Malinowski, 'Betontechnische Problemlösungen bei antiken Wasserbauten' in *Mitteilungen aus dem Leichtweiss-Institut*, Heft 64/1979, Braunschweïg.

5. K.M. Kenyon, *Archaeology in the Holy Land*, E. Benn, London, 1970.

6. H. Fahlbush and R. Malinowski, *Untersuchungen des Dichtungsmörtels von 5 geschichtlichen Rohrleitungen im ägäisch anatolischen Raum*, Leichtweiss-Institut für Wasserbau, Braunschweïg, 1981.

7. C. Wetter, The possibility of dating Roman monuments built of Opus Caementitium by analysing the mortar. Swedish Archeological Institut in Rome, XII, pp. 45–66, 1979.

8. H. Lamprecht, *Opus Cementitium Flieger*, Düsseldorf, 1968, pp. 22–5.

9. G.M. Idorn, 'The history of concrete technology — through a microscope' in *Beton-Technik*, No. 4, 1959.

10. A. Evans, *The Palace of Minos at Knossos*, Vol. 3, London, 1930, pp. 252–61.

11. H. Fahlbusch, *Vergleich antiker griechischer und römischer Wasserversorgungsanlagen*, Braunschweig, 1982, pp. 53–4.

12. G. Sandström, *Byggarna*, Interpublishing, Stockholm, 1968.

13. W.B. Dinsmoor, *The Architecture of Ancient Greece*, Batsford Ltd, London, p. 177.

The Origin of Gearing

VERNARD FOLEY, WERNER SOEDEL, JOHN
TURNER AND BRIAN WILHOITE

Current understanding of the origin and use of gears in classical antiquity rests mainly on three studies. That of Drachmann[1] relies chiefly on the literary remains, classifies the main types of gear applications and clarifies their chronology. Price's work[2] has extended this by explaining the nature and function of the famous Antikythera mechanism. The researches of Sleeswyk[3,4] have broken new ground in the detailed understanding of sophisticated ancient gearing and have contributed fundamentally to our knowledge of Chinese gear development.

Drachmann's major conclusions[5] regarding the use of ancient gears are summarized by him as follows:

> There are four different ways to use cog-wheels for transmission: parallel wheels engaging each other; wheels at right angles engaging each other; a wheel engaging a rack; a screw engaging a wheel: the endless screw.

Price assumes the validity of this scheme[6] and its associated chronology in determining the place of the Antikythera mechanism in the history of ancient technology. The first toothed wheels which can be verified from reasonably clear literary references appear in connection with racks and date from the work of Ctesibius about 280 B.C. Next comes the endless screw, or worm gear, known from the work of Archimedes and hence dating from a few decades later. Toothed wheels engaging each other in a common plane, such as the Antikythera mechanism displays, are first confirmed in the succeeding century by that same device. Tradition connects its invention with Archimedes, however. Gears whose planes meet at right angles are first described by Vitruvius about 25 B.C. There are a few earlier references to mechanisms that may employ gearing, but as these mostly refer simply to 'wheels', Drachmann has excluded them from consideration. He takes the presence or absence of references to teeth to be decisive in this selection.

It is significant that the earliest applications of gears seem not to involve pairs, but rather single gears interacting with other elements such as racks or worms. From this it can be seen that Drachmann's classification lacks completeness, for it omits sprocket wheels which mesh with chains. If toothed wheels count as gears when paired with racks and worms, there seems to be no valid reason for omitting the cases where they work with chains. And since chain-gear systems use gears operating singly rather than in meshed pairs, these might well fall into the earlier states of development and hence shed new light on the first steps toward gearing.

Outside the context of western civilization, gearing appears to have come

Figure 1. At left is the water-powered chain of pots water lifter described by Philo of Byzantium in his *Pneumatica*, as reconstructed by his editor, Carra de Vaux. The water wheel axle, at the bottom, carries two pulleys which power the top axle by means of twin chain drives. For Carra de Vaux, these chains were of the ordinary metallic, closed-link variety, and no explicit provision was made to keep them from slipping on the pulleys. At right is our reinterpretation of Philo's text. The chain here is of the flat-link form, for which change there is textual evidence. We hypothesize that its links possessed projections to forestall slipping, that these lay in the plane of the chain loop, and that the pulleys were recessed to accept them. The prismatic interiors of the pulleys were made pentagonal, after the example of the Nemi pump (Figure 3), but Philo does not specify a number. The projections could equally well protrude normally to the chain loop, as in the similar design in Fig. 9. Many aspects of our design are shown schematically, and not necessarily to scale.

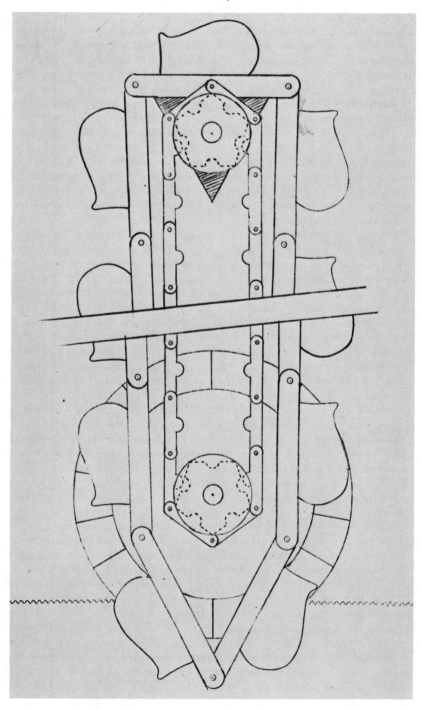

into use at about the same time. Needham[7] reports archaeological finds of Chinese gears dating from about 230 B.C. It is difficult to say how these were used, as only the isolated metallic gears themselves, or the moulds used to produce them, have survived from this early period. Note will be taken below of other Chinese developments as the occasion warrants, however.

It is well known that chains were used for power transmission in antiquity. Vitruvius[8] describes a chain of pots pump as having a double chain of iron placed around an axle located at the top of the pump assembly. There is no lower axle, the chain merely looping down into the water and rising again, carrying its bronze buckets downward to fill and upward to empty. The axle is turned by men treading a wheel. In a variation on this system he recommends placing a wheel with paddles fixed to its perimeter in the current of a river so that it may be turned without human labour. It is not fully clear from this second description whether the buckets are attached to a chain or to the wheel itself.

Fortunately, Philon remedies this deficiency. Writing in his *Pneumatica*[9] about 230–200 B.C., he describes a chain of pots pump driven by a water wheel. The axle of this wheel somehow drives an axle further up, at the top of the assembly, which carries a triangular prism. This prism turns the chain of pots, which loops freely down into the water as before. Unfortunately, Philon does not clearly describe the drive system which enables the lower axle, driven by the wheel, to turn the upper one and thus the pot chain. Both axles carry a pair of *bakarat*, which translates as *pulleys*. Each pulley pair has lying on them an 'iron device . . . resembling a column (ba‘mond)'. A problem in the adjacent text makes it difficult to determine the precise nature of this iron device like a column, but Carra de Vaux has ingeniously surmised that it resembled a spinal column, or a string of vertebrae. This seems apt, as it was made of segments, pivoted on rivets or nails (*masāmīr*). This would imply something like a flat link chain. His drawings show a chain of conventional closed-loop links, but it is obvious that his artist has taken liberties with the original manuscript illustrations. His version, together with our pictorial reinterpretation of his text, are shown together as our Fig. 1. We are grateful to our Purdue University History Department colleague, Professor Robert A. McDaniel, for providing us with these translations.

It is particularly interesting that the pulley drive system may have struck Philon as resembling a spinal column. Vertebral columns, of course, show the same principle of flexibly-joined individual rigid units as chains display. Additionally, in many vertebrates the individual vertebrae show prominent projections. Some are lateral and form the attachment point for the ribs. Others, such as the human spinous processes, form freestanding dorsal prominences when the tissues have been separated from the bones.[10] Since Philon's water lifter was driven by the river, it may have generated several horsepower and special provision may have been necessary to prevent the drive system from slipping under load on the rounded circumference of the pulleys. It is plausible to think that projections on the individual links may have engaged depressions cut into the pulley to accomplish this end. At the very least, the groove on the rim of the pulley, which surely was standard by this time, could have engaged the projections in order to keep the chain from slipping sideways off the pulley rim. Philon's date is approximately 220 B.C.,[11] and pulleys are described in the pseudo-Aristotelian *Mechanical Problems* of *c*. 300 B.C.[12]

It thus seems reasonable to think of Philon's chain of pots pump as employing a flat-link chain drive between the pulleys. Certainly the pot chain itself has that construction. Its links correspond in length to the sides of the triangular prism carried on the upper axle of the system, plus an allowance for the angle through which they must bend. The sharpness of this angle is sufficient to deter slipping and makes it more likely that the column allusion is intended to be applied to the chains for the pulleys rather than the one for the pots.

Hence, in comparison to the chain of pots lifter in Vitruvius, Philon's is clearly more sophisticated. Vitruvius does not mention any particular means of securing his chains against slipping around their axle. At most, the axle was perhaps faceted, or may simply have utilized friction.

Once again it is interesting to compare Chinese developments. Needham[13] describes a traditional design of water lifter developed there which used a chain whose links carried flat paddles, rectangular in outline, moving up within an inclined trough and back down again below it. The first clear evidence for its existence comes from the first and second centuries A.D., although a rather vague literary allusion from a fourth-century B.C. source is traditionally held to describe it. Originally foot-powered, it had been mechanized by about 965, when drawings of oxen working it through gears meshing at right angles first begin to appear. In its earlier form, however, the treadle shaft carried projections that fit in between the paddles to force the chain's movements. Thus it employed prototypical gears, and its earliness in the Chinese technical context complements the use of chains with gears in the western setting. And finally, it is of particular interest, given the description of Philon's chains as 'columns', that the traditional Chinese nickname for the paddle chain lifter is *lung ke chhê*, or 'dragon backbone machine'.

The date of Philon's writing, the late third century B.C.,[14] makes it competitive with all but Ctesibius as a record for the initial stages of gear design in the west. Even in comparison with Ctesibius, it conveys the impression of an earlier state in gear evolution, for another of Philon's pumps (Fig. 2) uses a rack and pinion actuating system.[15] The pinion is made of a disc with handspikes around its edge, and these engage pegs fixed to the outside of a hollow shaft which reaches down to the main pump chamber under the surface. When the pinion is oscillated, the whole pump assembly is moved up and down. As Drachmann[5] has noted, this is clearly a primitive arrangement in comparison to the use of a piston sliding in a fixed cylinder, the arrangement to which Ctesibius owes a good part of his fame. Hence, here also, Philon's text seems to preserve the technical tradition of an earlier time.

It is true that portions of Philon's manuscript, even in the oldest extant

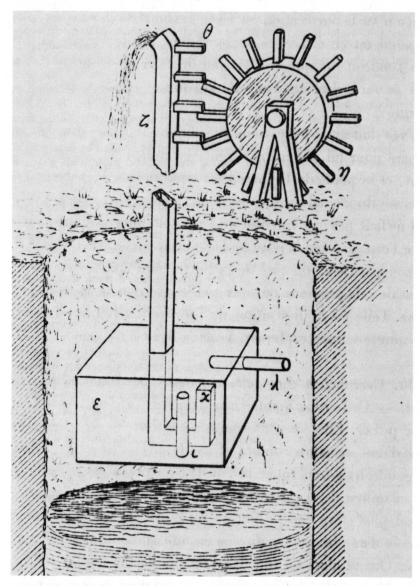

Figure 2. A primitive form of water pump from the *Pneumatica* of Philo of Byzantium. In the box at the bottom is the mechanism which is somehow intended to admit water and to discharge it up the standpipe as the pipe and box are reciprocated vertically. The extra mass which must be moved in this process, in comparison to a pump having a fixed pipe and cylinder, with the piston being reciprocated inside by a separate rod, makes the design appear to be older than the invention of the piston by Ctesibius. In the present context the design is chiefly interesting because it uses a rack and pinion.

versions, contain later Arabic interpolations. If the chain of pots pump were to fall into this category, part of the present argument would be invalidated. Drachmann[16] is the main prior source of comment on this point, and he was of two minds about the chain of pots pump, calling it a 'queer hybrid'. Parts of it seemed to be very old, such as the water wheel, which was made of radiating ladles rather than conventional buckets or vanes. The inefficiencies of this design required a strong current. The use of a triangular prism also seemed to him to bear the stamp of high antiquity.

Drachmann took the drive for the pots, however, to involve ordinary chain running over ordinary wheels and this to him seemed much later. As we have already seen, a close analysis of the text lends itself to an alternative explanation. But Drachmann believed that the pot drive must be younger than Philon, since the latter, writing later in his *Belopoeica*,[17] used a crude flat-linked chain running over pentagons to cycle the mechanism of a repeating catapult. For Drachmann, the failure of Erwin Schramm to devise a working model of this system cast doubt on the ability of the ancients to construct such a machine. Hence, by implication, this part of the water lifter system must be of Arabic origin. As will be seen below, the results of our tests cast a strong doubt on these conclusions. Hence for us Philon's chain of pots pump is not 'an ancient instrument, possibly partly improved by a later hand', as Drachmann believed but a device whose workability gives it a claim to being as old as any of the rest of the manuscript.

All of which suggests that further light on the origin of gearing in the west might be found by considering the early development of gears which operate together with chains. Some of these are prismatic and have as 'teeth' only their vertices. This crudity, however, might well be a mark of their antiquity, if their efficiency could be otherwise demonstrated.

Additional support for this view comes from the fragments which Uccelli[18] reconstructed as a chain of pots pump used to bail the bilge of one of the Nemi ships (Fig. 3). Most of the discussion surrounding this find has centred around whether it was turned with a crank or handspikes.[19] In the present context it is of greatest interest because the pot chain appears to have been looped at its upper end around a pentagonal prism, deeply cut away in five radially-symmetrical places to receive the buckets. Although this superficially resembles a gear of the modern sort, it is in fact what might be called a negative or inverted gear, for the projections are the buckets on the chain and the tooth-equivalents on the prism are recessed. There is no doubt that this design would work. It is the ordinary arrangement used today for driving the chains of chain saws and it is quite close in form to a conventional sprocket. Slight changes in the geometry of the pots and their connecting linkage would be all that was required to make it operate as these do. The wear incident to normal operation could probably effect such changes.

The Nemi ships have been tentatively dated to the time of Caligula, or around A.D. 45–55,[20] which is too late to enable the bailer to shed much direct light on the origin of gearing. As indirect evidence, however, it can indicate the possibility of earlier developments in power transmission that may be closely related to the history of gearing.

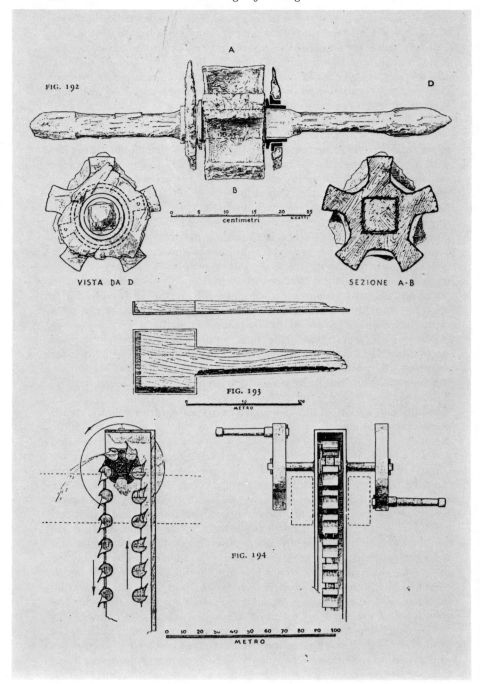

Figure 3. Fragments from one of the Nemi ships, reconstructed by Uccelli as components of a bailing pump. The driving assembly is radially pentagonal.

Stronger evidence for the priority of prisms and chains comes from the time of one Dionysius of Alexandria. As we have noted above, Philon describes in his *Belopoeica*[21] a repeating catapult invented by one Dionysius which employs a chain and prism actuating mechanism. The dates of Dionysius unfortunately cannot be established with exactness. Since he preceded Philon, he would seem to be at least a contemporary of Archimedes, and perhaps even of Ctesibius. Both of the attempts made thus far to date him more accurately put him even earlier. Pauly and Wissowa suggest that his machine was invented during the siege of Rhodes by Demetrius Poliorcetes in 305-4 B.C.[22] Marsden tentatively identified him with an engineer of the same name who supervised the transport of a large statue from Sinope to Alexandria during the reign of Ptolemy I, who ruled until about 282 B.C.[23] If either of these is correct, his reported system might antedate all known forms of toothed gearing.

His catapult itself is so extraordinary as to merit a brief description. Our Fig. 4 from an earlier study is not fully representative of the way we would now interpret the machine, but helps to clarify its operation. Other drawings, neither completely accurate from our viewpoint, are given by Marsden[24] and Schramm.[25] Arrows were loaded into a vertical magazine above the main catapult assembly, and were fed one at a time by a revolving valve on to a firing trough. This trough reciprocated just under the plane swept out by the bowstring as it fired. A claw on the top of the trough, opened and closed automatically by pins on the fixed part of the frame, seized, pulled back and released the bowstring. A finger on the reciprocating trough engaged a helical groove cut into the valve so as to release arrows, one at a time, at the proper moment. These were kept in an 'upper case', or magazine, which was mounted just above the 'lower case', or frame, of the machine. In order to reciprocate the trough, Dionysius used a chain and prism drive. Philon's account of it[17] runs as follows:

> It did not have a cord pull-back system; but the windlass had projections at each side, constructed in the form of pentagons: there were oaken, iron plated frames, joined to each other and held together by pins, and these were wrapped around the windlass. They were placed on both sides of the case, as is the usual practice for the pulling forward system in other engines, their ends were bound with iron plates and they were attached to the slider by means of a headed pin which was caught in a socket [i.e. in the slider]. The little frames had some projecting parts working in the gap between the cases; a groove was made in the side of the [lower] case, around the windlass, equal in depth to the extent of the projections, so that the little frames would have free room to revolve around the axle. The pull back system was so arranged round the windlass that a man pulling the hand-spikes from the forward position towards himself ran the claw forward and, vice versa, pushing them from the rear position withdrew it and effected the firing.

If anything, this device was too successful. Philon saw it and found little

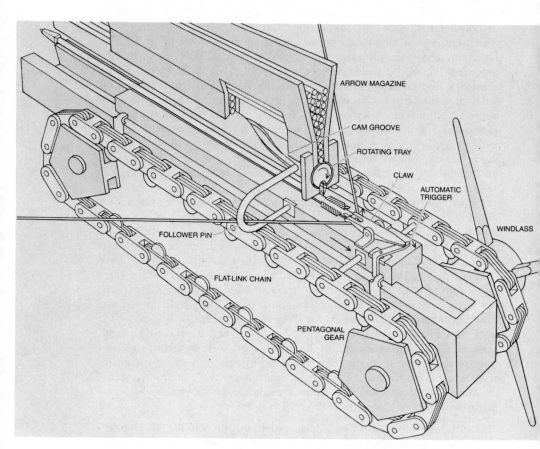

Labels on figure: ARROW MAGAZINE, CAM GROOVE, ROTATING TRAY, CLAW, AUTOMATIC TRIGGER, WINDLASS, FOLLOWER PIN, FLAT-LINK CHAIN, PENTAGONAL GEAR

Figure 4. An interpretation, previously published by Soedel and Foley, of the repeating catapult of Dionysius of Alexandria. For purposes of clarity, several dimensional liberties have taken with the layout of the machine. Arrows stored in its magazine are fed one at a time to the reciprocating firing guide by the 180-degree turning of the rotating tray. This rotation is accomplished by a metal finger attached to the firing guide, and working in a helical groove in the tray. In the illustration this groove was mistakenly terminated by our artist at the point where the finger contracts it. In practice, the groove must extend farther to the rear. As the firing guide reciprocated in the fixed stock of the weapon, fixed projections on the stock rotate the automatic trigger of the weapon, causing its claw to alternately grip and release the bowstring.

The reciprocation of the firing tray is accomplished by a chain-prism drive system, probably actuated by a windlass. In this earlier interpretation, the projections on the flat-link chain were assumed to engage recesses cut into the pentagons. An alternative interpretation developed here is depicted in Fig. 6. From Werner Soedel and Vernard Foley, 'Ancient Catapults', Copyright 1979 by *Scientific American*, Inc.

fault with its mechanical arrangement. But it had such accuracy and it fired so fast that it tended to waste ammunition. This, combined with a range of one stade, or about 185 m, which was inferior to the single-shot catapult, combined to limit its role to a very modest one. After Philon's time it is not heard of again.

The first attempt to reconstruct the device seems to have been made by Erwin Schramm,[26] who could not get the pull-back system to work. Accordingly he had his workmen replace it with bicycle sprockets and chains, whereupon it functioned flawlessly. Once when he was demonstrating it before Kaiser Wilhelm, it obligingly rose to the occasion and split one of its arrows with the following one. Schramm's findings are reinforced by experience with a model constructed to about one-sixth scale by Turner. He did not attempt to make the chain and prism arrangement work on this small scale, but used sprockets and conventional chains. Aside from this, the model is authentic and works adequately well to prove the functionality of the design.

Later published scholarly opinion on the pull-back system has been mixed. Drachmann reported Schramm's negative results without further significant comment.[27] Marsden thought the system would work but did not try to build it.[28] He proposed changing the pentagons to decagons, a change which in our experience would seriously impair its functioning. In a previous publication, two of the authors proposed saving the appearances by modelling the pull-back system after the fashion of the Nemi ship pump.[29]

As noted above, there is no doubt that this would give a functional arrangement. A closer subsequent look at Philon's text, however, suggested an alternate reconstruction which has proved to be functional in a full-scale model and which agrees more closely with the text than did our first attempt.

The key feature of the text is the projections (*hyperochas*) which are found on the links of the chain. In their first attempt (Fig. 4), Soedel and Foley took some liberties with the text and made these protrude in the plane of the chain loop, where they could function like the buckets of the Nemi ship bailer or like the implied projections of Philon's pump. This seemed especially suitable since both the Nemi bailer and Dionysius' pull-back system used pentagons. But two aspects of the arrangement suggest a different location for the projections.

First, Philon says they run in the space between the cases. This implies that they slide in a gap left between the framework which holds the slider and the arrow magazine directly above it. Hence the projections protrude normal to the chain loop plane, rather than lying within it. Such a view is reinforced by Philon's statement that a groove has to be cut in the lower stock, around the windlass axle, to let them slide through.

In this orientation it seemed unlikely that the projections could engage in notches cut in the pentagons. Nor did they seem to effect any connection between the chains and the sliding trough. This was done by the headed pin which the text describes. And since the text seems to say that at least several of the frames had projections, it seemed further unlikely that these were fixed to the slider. If they did, when they came to the arc round the windlass the machine would jam. What then was their role?

Philon's text implies that the groove round the windlass must be made an easy fit for the projections. But he might not have fully understood their function, or he may have lacked the language to speak of what today might be called a close-running fit. For if the projections were made so that they slid through the groove in continuous contact with its sides, they would compel the links of the chain to lie flat against the flats of the pentagons and so keep the system from slipping.

To think of this more clearly (Fig. 5), imagine a flat-link chain wrapped around a prism, loaded at one end and hanging free at the other. As the load causes the chain to begin to slip, the first link following the first bend made in the chain by the prism on the loaded side will begin to pivot away from contact with the prism face. If this pivoting can be stopped, the cramping of the chain pivots around the vertices of the prism will prevent any slipping. This is particularly true of prisms of few sides. Their angles are sharper, hence they can be made with fits loose enough to permit easy

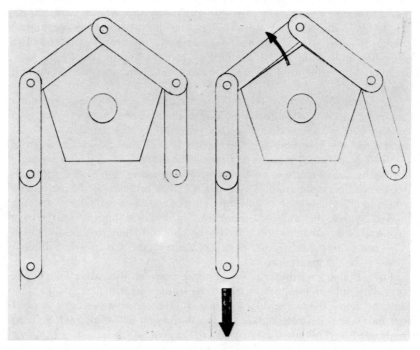

Figure 5. At the left, a pentagonal prism with links sized to lie cramped around its vertices without requiring slippage. The endmost unbent links of the chain stand slightly free of the vertices. When a load is applied to the chain, as at right, the first bent link tends in consequence to pivot around the vertex, slightly displacing the adjacent cramped links also. If projections on the links can arrest this pivoting, slippage will be less likely to occur.

operation, while continuing to grip the chain well. Hence it appears that Philon's choice of the triangle for the driving prism of the pot chain may not have been an idle one.

Testing done on a model made by Willhoite, using wooden links running around a pentagonal prism, confirmed these suppositions. Even without projections on its links this was able to support about 13 kg on one side of the chain while the other end, which weighed less than a kilogram, dangled freely in the air. When projections taking the form of pins running through the centre of the links parallel to the hinge pins were installed and confined by camming surfaces to an arc which pressed them closely against the prism, the assembly succeeded in raising about 35 kg. At that point, failure of the wooden links began to occur.

On the strength of these favourable results, a full-scale model with metal reinforcement of the links was constructed by Foley (Fig. 6). The projections were made 3.175 mm thick, and of mild steel. Each link measured 87 mm between hinge pin centres, and its projections engaged a groove with a radius of 48.25 mm. These last two dimensions can be deduced from Philon's description of the repeater. The system was designed so that the wooden portions of the links were non-load bearing, all stresses being taken by the steel bolts and straps. The rubbing surfaces of the projections were milled into arcs so as to give a smoother sliding engagement with their groove.

To determine whether this design would function as Philon said it did, it was necessary to estimate the stresses to which it was subjected. The only

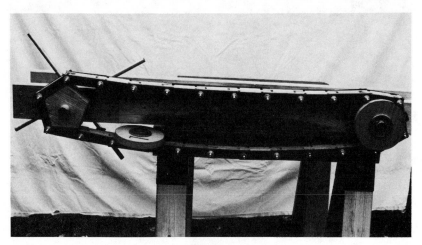

Fig. 6a

Figure 6. In (a) the complete pull-back assembly is shown, with one disc removed to reveal the pentagonal prism. Illustration (b) shows a prism with the chain removed, so that the groove which confines the link projections can be seen. In (c) the chain has been slipped partway off, showing the engagement of a projection with the groove. Photo (d) shows a view down the chain, with projections lying on the prism flats and receding into the distance.

Fig. 6b

Fig. 6c

Fig. 6d

data that bear on this are his statements[30] that the repeater fired a bolt one cubit and one dactyl in length (about 480 mm) for a maximum distance of a little over a stade (let us call this 200 m). As was pointed out above, one of the reasons for its lack of success was that standard catapults could fire much further.

In late medieval England, archers were accustomed to practice with their longbows, using arrows heavy enough to inure them to battle conditions, at distances in excess of 220 m.[31] From this it would appear that the bow of the repeater catapult was of a draw weight that could be managed by a hand-bow archer. Examples of surviving medieval longbows are rare, but estimates of their draw weight have been made, and these range from 34 to 45.5 kg.[32] These weights correspond well to the upper range of handbow draw weights considered feasible today.[33] Thus if Dionysius' chains and prisms could sustain approximately 50 kg without slipping they could probably provide the performance level reported by Philon. Since two chains were used, one on each side of the machine, each would be loaded to about 25 kg.

The full-sized single chain and prism system of the reconstruction proved capable of raising and holding 100 kg without letting the load slip. At this load level, however, friction was very high and certainly would have impeded the rapid operation of the machine which was, after all, presumably one of the chief reasons for its complex design. In fact, the rubbing of the link projections against their groove began to make itself felt substantially as soon as the load on the chain reached 30–40 kg.

Thus we suggest that a major reason for the limited success of the repeater was the energy ceiling imposed on its bow by the inefficiencies of its pull-back systems. If the pull-back system significantly slowed the operation of the repeater, then it would become inferior to a single-shot machine which could be cocked more rapidly and then loaded with an arrow by hand.

In this chain-prism system, the greater the load, the greater the force pressing the link projections against the outer walls of the confining groove, for a given prism choice. For prisms of smaller numbers of sides, the rubbing is lighter because the half-link lengths are shorter. In conventional gearing, of course, this rubbing effect is not found at all. Obviously, then, prism gearing represents a more primitive way of transmitting power than with a chain and toothed sprockets. This conclusion, in turn, reinforces the prism's claim to antedate toothed gears and strengthens the probability that it was an ancestor. If toothed gears had been in existence, surely Dionysius would have used them instead.

For all their inefficiency, however, some of the parts of the pull-back system convey a hint that they may have been rationally designed. Marsden suggested replacing their pentagons with decagons, but the text clearly specifies the former shape, and several considerations imply that this choice may have been a deliberate one. First, as has been noticed, the Nemi bailer uses a pentagonal arrangement. Second, Philon specifies that the gap between the catapult frame and its arrow magazine suspended just above was about one dactyl, which is approximately 19.3 mm.[34] He believed that this gap was left for the operation of the bowstring, but a bow of the weight needed to achieve the performance he reports cannot have needed a string so thick as this.

Now it can be observed that as the prisms turn they force the chain to travel at rhythmically varying heights from the line connecting the two prism axles (Fig. 7). The reason is inherent in the prism shape, for it has two radii, one connecting its centre with its vertices, and the other, the apothem,

Fig. 7a

Fig. 7b

Figure 7. In (a) the chain is shown bent around a prism vertex, with one link just entering its confining groove. This end of the chain has now been raised to its maximum height. In (b) the endmost unbent link lies straight along a prism flat. The chain's height is now minimal at this end.

with the midpoints of its sides. When the pull comes straight along a link lying flat against a prism face, the chain will lie closer to the windlass axle than when the pull comes off a vertex whose radius is normal to the line of force. This varying radius means that even with a uniform prism axle speed there will be variations in the velocity with which the chain travels. In practice, it means that the chain will move in a somewhat jerky fashion. This rising, falling and jerking of the chain can be mitigated somewhat if the two prisms are placed out of phase with each other, but it will always be present and requires a clearance for the travel of the projections between the prisms which is substantially wider than their thickness.

Obviously the velocity variations created by the rotation of these prisms, and the clearances required for chains wrapped around them, are two aspects of the same situation. Minimizing velocity change is reasonably important for the smooth and reliable operation of the repeater mechanism. Turner's scale model shows this quite clearly in its functioning. The matter of clearance might be thought to be more arbitrary, but it is not completely so. If the chains require more gap in which to lash up and down, the mechanism can to some degree be rearranged so as to accommodate them. Its arrangement becomes more awkward, however, in the case of the square, and for the case of the triangle appears to become nearly mechanically impossible, at least if one desires durability and reasonably rational design.

In the case of the chosen prism, the pentagon, its dimensions can be determined from the fact that the board against which it lies is 5 dactyls (96.5 mm) wide. Since Philon says that the projections, after they emerge from their clearance groove around the windlass axle, run along the top of this board, it can be assumed that the apothem of the pentagon is equal to half the width of the board, or about 48.25 mm. (If the projections travelled at a significant distance above the edge of the board, or more than was required for them to clear the board when the adjacent prism had one of its flats uppermost, they would not be confined as quickly by the groove, nor confined for as many degrees of rotation, as if their underneath clearance were minimized. Hence, they would be more likely to slip.) For a pentagon of this size, the clearance required for the rising and falling of the chain is about 11.5 mm. Adding to this something for the thickness of the projections, say 6 or 7 mm, brings us near the dactyl clearance which Philon reported. Hence there appears to be no corruption regarding the number of prism sides reported in his text.

If a prism of more than five sides had been chosen by Dionysius, the clearance gap for the projections would of course have been reduced. But if this were so, the chain links would not have been as sharply cramped around the prism as with a pentagon, and their ability to resist slipping would have been reduced. In addition, as the number of sides of the prism increased, the length of each side would have decreased and, with it, the length of the links of the surrounding chain. This would have put the projection on each link closer to the prism vertices as each of these came under load. For a given load, we assume that the width of the metal strapping of the links was constant. Thus, as the prism face number increased, the changing ratio of the arm of loading to the arm of resistance in the lever system involved would mean that the projections were pressed ever more forcefully against their groove, creating more friction. Hence, as noted above, greater friction drag would be encountered by prisms of more sides.

Table 1 and its accompanying graphs summarize the relationships among these four factors — projection drag levels, resistance to slipping, smoothness of motion and needed clearance — for prisms of three to eight sides, sized so as to fit the catapult's frame. Drag level data is given as the mechanical advantage of the link projections to that of their applied load. Slipping resistance is given by the absolute value of the cosine of the angle included by two links when one is bent around the prism and its neighbour is both in line with the applied load and flush against a prism face. Velocity changes are given by the ratio between the two radii of the polygon involved, and clearance requirements by the difference of these same two radii.

In making these calculations we assumed that the endmost unbent link in each chain lay flush against the topmost face of its prism. The projection on the adjacent link was assumed, for simplicity's sake, to contact its groove at a point 3.175 mm radially outward from the centre of that side. We assumed, in other words, a chain of a constant link width and projections of a constant size. The loading lever arm was assumed to be 12.7 mm.

In comparing physical relationships like this, one is often at something of a loss as to how to size the scales. In this case we have simply laid out the right- and left-hand scales in each graph so as to have the same range. The only exception to this was in the case of slippage tendency where, in going from the square to the triangle, an entirely new geometrical relationship begins. We left the triangle off the scale. Given the arbitrary nature of our scale selection, the results can only be suggestive. It is, however, of interest that our curves of advantage and disadvantage bracket the pentagonal region. Since this is the case, we have some leeway in the matter of scaling assumptions, in the use or non-use of lubrication in the original, in differences in the grade of workmanship between the original and our reconstruction, and so on.

Hence prisms with fewer sides than five are less prone to slippage than is the pentagon but less smooth than it is in their operation. Again, prisms having more than five faces require less travelling space for their chains, but when under increasing load they develop high friction loads more quickly than pentagons do. Thus the pentagonal prism seems a reasonable compromise design and may well have been a deliberate choice. It gives a good balance of smooth operation, slippage resistance, neat chain installation and low link projection drag.

This analysis suggests in turn that ancient bronze gearing, with its teeth made in the form of equilateral triangles, might have been developed in an attempt to combine the slippage resistance of prisms with few sides, and the smoothness of operation of prisms of many sides. Placing the triangle, the prism of minimal sides, on the circumference of the circle, the prism having, as it were, an infinite number of sides, would be a logical way to attempt achieving this end.

TABLE 1

Number of Prism Sides	Projection Drag under Load	Slipping Resistance	Velocity Variation	Clearance Needed
3	0.621	—	2.0	0.289
4	0.540	1.0	1.41	0.207
5	0.416	0.95	1.23	0.162
6	0.363	0.87	1.15	0.134
7	0.270	0.79	1.11	0.114
8	0.158	0.71	1.08	0.099

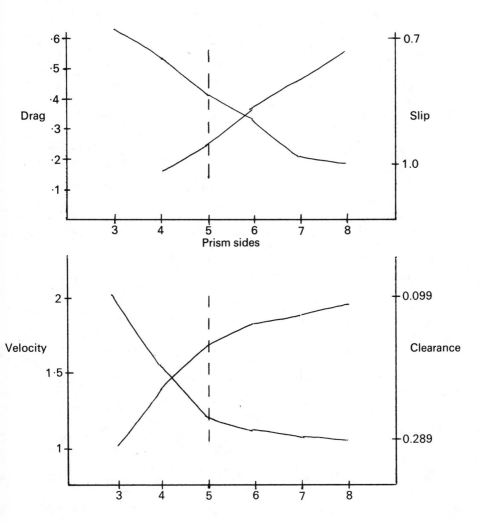

Pot chain water lifters possess one other mechanical feature which reinforces the hypothesis that they were instrumental in the development of gearing. As Drachmann has pointed out,[35] in several Greek mechanical texts the word used for gear tooth is *skutalion*, which means a round stick or handspike. He deduced from this term and from drawings in the manuscript of Heron's *Pneumatics* that some of the early gears were made of discs of wood thick enough to have pegs solidly driven into their edges or faces. Much the same technique was used for constructing the driving system of the Chinese 'dragon backbone machine', except that here the projections were rectangular in section rather than round.[36] They projected radially from the driving axle and bore against the paddles which were fixed to the chain. With this construction the geared water mill of Vitruvius would certainly have been a feasible proposition, as countless examples from the millwork of later centuries show. Whether Vitruvius' mill would have worked with the equilateral triangular teeth which are the main metallic gear rivals to the peg gear in antiquity is most doubtful. Such gears would have developed considerable thrusts normal to their planes when engaging at right angles. Sleeswyk[3,4] has ingeniously used such gears in his reconstruction of the odometer described in Vitruvius, and has very plausibly decided that the Vitruvian term *localumentum* referred to portions of the enclosing framework designed to keep such gears from slipping out of engagement. The odometer, however, worked under very light loads and whether such tooth engagements could efficiently transmit enough power to grind grain seems questionable.

The gear with triangular teeth can now be dated fairly securely from the time of Archimedes. Price's work with the Antikythera mechanism, together with Sleeswyk's treatment of the Vitruvian odometer, strongly suggest this provenance. The surviving fragments of the Antikythera mechanism are of bronze. The earliest Chinese gear survivals are also of bronze, as both the gears themselves and their ceramic casting moulds testify. The peg gear, by contrast, from its very form must have been made of wood, and thus would not be so likely to leave behind definite evidence of its invention.[37] Hence its age is less definite than that of the metallic form. It was until lately still used in the irrigation wheels of the Mediterranean, but these cannot be dated to a precise beginning in either the animal- or human-powered form. The water-powered version of this gear pair given in Vitruvius may be among the earliest of its kind, or it may simply be one of the first in a much older tradition to be joined with such power. It is highly suggestive, however, that the oldest gear system in Drachmann's category, that which engages a rack, was almost certainly made using pegs. The necessities of dealing with the grain of the wood would require this for the rack if it were to be at all heavily loaded, and using pegs would certainly simplify the construction of the gear teeth. As noted above, peg gears are much less critical in their meshing geometry than gears with equilateral triangle projections. Hence in comparing the peg gear with the triangular toothed version it seems the older of the two forms.

Thus it is interesting to note that the lantern gear is closely associated with chain of pots water lifters for as far back as the manuscript illustration tradition will take us. In this gear form a peg gear with its rounds driven into the disc face rather than its edge obtains support for the otherwise freestanding ends of the pegs by inserting them in holes bored in a second disc installed adjacently upon the gear shaft. Unfortunately, the manuscript tradition does not extend in an unbroken way back to antiquity. Ramelli,[38] Besson,[39] and other Renaissance engineers show such lifters. The earliest example known to the authors is from the *Bellifortis* of Konrad Kyeser aus Eichstat,[40] written about 1404. As Gille[41] has pointed out, however, the manuscript tradition in these medieval works frequently derives from lost ancient originals. This would appear to be the case for Kyeser, for his tympanum water lifter and his Archimedean screw could have been used to illustrate Vitruvius with almost no change.

It is important, then, that in these late medieval and early modern chain of pots designs a lantern pinion serves as the topmost assembly, and sometimes also as the bottom one, around which the pot chain turns. Frequently the chain links are equipped with projections that fit between the pinion bars to keep the chains from slipping. One of the lifters illustrated from Ramelli (Fig. 8) gives an example,[38] and the other (Fig. 9) shows how the Nemi pump arrangements may have evolved. These link projections may well be descended from the crucial link projections in Dionysius' catapult pull-back system, altered slightly in their geometry so as to engage what is now a skeletal prism rather than a solid one, a step foreshadowed in the bailer of the Nemi ship. They could have descended to the Renaissance through either the manuscript or the craft tradition.

From putting projections on the chain links to putting them on the prism is an easy step once the prism has been excavated or skeletized. An alternate origin for the toothed wheel is at hand in the circular ratchet, however. These were used on catapults certainly by the time of Vitruvius, and perhaps as early as around 200 B.C.[14] They may have been used on cranes at an even earlier period. Probably they originally evolved from sticks or loops of rope used to snub the handspikes of windlasses.

All this seems to imply that the origin of gearing may be found in devices of a utilitarian sort. Price has emphasized the close connection of metallic triangular tooth gearing with what he calls a high technology tradition.[42] In his view, gears developed in close association with pure thought, the abstract sciences and virtuoso mathematical instruments. Thus Price draws a firm line between Archimedes and the Antikythera mechanism on the one hand, and the ancient tradition of useful engineering on the other.

Several recent researches suggest that the ancient technological realities may not have been so clearly divided. Sleeswyk,[43] for example, has advanced quite plausible reasons for assuming that the mileage-measuring cart in Vitruvius, with its extremely high-reduction gear train, was an invention of Archimedes. He has ingeniously reconstructed these gears as hypoidal, an arrangement which complements the mechanical virtuosity previously attributed to Archimedes in connection with the worm gear. More specifically, Sleeswyk suggests that Archimedes designed the cart around 260 B.C., close

Figure 8. A chain of pots pump from Ramelli. Note at the lower left that each chain link is equipped with a projection which hooks between the bars of the lantern pinions of the assembly, shown above seperately at H. Slack in the chain assembly is removed by the nuts D and Z.

Figure 9. An excavator on the chain of pots principle, from Ramelli. Here slippage is defeated by projections on the chain links which protrude normal to the chain loop. The recesses cut into S, shown at the top of the assembly, to accept these projections, convert it into a prototypical gear, shown seperately at V below.

to the beginning of his career, and at about the same time that the Romans were extending their highway system southward along the Italian boot to the straits of Messina, the better to communicate with what were at the time their Syracusan allies, who also supplied them with crucial military equipment.

Sleeswyk's argument rests in good measure upon the fact that the mileage-cart registers the completion of a mile's travel by dropping a pebble into a resonant bronze vessel. Arabic sources attribute the same sounding system to a water clock they trace back to Archimedes. By this means the driver of the cart would be made aware that the time had come to put another milestone in place. And Archimedes, a young engineer working for one of Rome's allies, might be seen as designing a system to make the job easier and more accurate by mechanizing it. Some quantitative support for this argument comes from the fact that the mileage-cart was designed for a total run, without resetting, of 400 miles, while the new highway system was of similar magnitude, about 375 miles.

Sleeswyk's argument can be strengthened by referring to the recent and crucial recasting of the traditional order of composition of Archimedes' works by Knorr.[44] By closely examining such aspects as the degree of sophistication of the exhaustion methods used by Archimedes to approximate the areas of figures bounded by curves, Knorr finds many reasons to significantly alter the traditional ordering established by Heath. In particular, Knorr believes that *Dimension of the Circle*, wherein Archimedes computes the value of pi to lie between $3\frac{1}{7}$ and $3\frac{10}{71}$, was among his very earliest surviving works.[45] Thus it dates from about the same time as the mileage-cart and the highway project.

This in turn suggests that Archimedes might have had a very practical reason for computing pi to such a close approximation. If the cart is to give accurate mileage readings, mechanical sources of error, particularly cumulative ones, must be minimized. We can tell from a passage in *Sand Reckoner*, where Archimedes describes how to measure the apparent diameter of the sun, that he was keenly aware of experimental errors in measuring and ingenious in doing away with them. Now gearing by its nature does not lead to cumulative error providing the teeth mesh without slipping. The construction of the wheels of the cart is much more crucial, particularly since the ancients were much more easily able to measure diameters of circles than their circumferences. The age of the steel tape was still in the future, the traveller wheel does not seem to have been in use, cords were susceptible to stretching, and horn and lead flexible rules[46] gave either difficulties in use or problems with progressive loss of accuracy. Hence the mileage-cart wheels were probably gauged by their diameter.

Thus an accurate determination of pi becomes crucial to the reliable functioning of the cart. In his report on the mileage-cart, Vitruvius was content to lay out its wheels using a quite rough approximation of pi.[47] Corruptions in his text present one with a choice of values, but the best appears to be 3.125.[48] With this value at the end of a 400-mile run, assuming nothing else went wrong, the cart's reading would be in error by a little more than two miles.

With Archimedes' values for pi the error might drop to less than a tenth of a mile. Indeed, Knorr has argued that Archimedes elsewhere carried his approximations of pi to levels more than twenty times as accurate as the upper and lower bounds given in *Dimension of the Circle*.[49] At any of these accuracy levels, however, the size of the wheel circumference would be far less important than irregularities caused by wheel wear, departure from truth or slippage, and even more crucial than these would be the differing speeds of the two wheels when the cart turned corners.

This point in turn recalls the differential gear mechanism in the Antikythera machine.[50] There is nothing in Vitruvius' report which suggests that the mileage-cart he knew had such sophistication, but he was writing almost two and a half centuries after the event and much might have been lost in the meantime. Or the differential gear idea might have been devised by Archimedes as a projected mileage-cart improvement which did not work out in practice, perhaps falling a prey to the rough road surfaces or the high-friction bearing designs of the time.

One must hasten to say that these arguments are all indirect, and there does not appear to be any specific concrete evidence for Archimedes' use of differential gearing in connection with mileage measuring. Sleeswyk's work on the related arrangements of Chinese south-pointing chariots,[47] however, though they date from a later period, suggests that we should be cautious about excluding the possibility of a useful knowledge origin for even sophisticated mechanical contrivances. The appearance of the mileage-cart early in Archimedes' career might mean that he could develop the idea of a wheel-motion averaging device over subsequent years or decades, to apply it later in a different mechanical context.

As the Antikythera mechanism itself has proved, and as the present effort attempts to show, the literary remains of antiquity by themselves are often a drastically inadequate guide to the ancient engineering realities and to the processes by which these came to be. In such cases wider surmises rather than narrower ones are a better guide to the uncovering of interesting patterns of interrelationships, so long as hypothesis is clearly labelled as such, and so long as it is kept within proper bounds. Hence our summarizing point is that a full reporting of the evolution of ancient gearing would now seem to require the consideration of both the 'High' and the 'Low' technological traditions, rather than dismissing the latter in a cursory way as uninteresting.

In conclusion, then, it would appear that the origin of western gearing is to be found in connection with utilitarian devices, and particularly with water lifters. The productivity increases which irrigation made possible were as high as eleven-fold when compared to dry-land farming,[51] and certainly such gains would have helped to stimulate a sustained level of interest and experiment, as well as the capital to back it. One should also recall that the Hellenistic period was one of urban expansion, with the heightened need for water supply which this entails.

Thus we propose that gearing is rather older than previously supposed, that it began with chains and prisms rather than with toothed wheels, and that it grew mainly out of water raising. Hence early gears are one more nail driven into the coffin of the idea that the Greek mind was so enamoured with scientific and philosophical theory that it had no patience with engineering.

Notes

1. A. G. Drachmann, *The Mechanical Technology of Greek and Roman Antiquity*, Munksgaard, Copenhagen, 1963, especially pp. 200–3.

2. Derek J. de Solla Price, *Gears From the Greeks*, Science History Publications, New York, 1975, especially pp. 53–60.

3. Andre Wegener Sleeswyk, 'Vitruvius' Waywiser' in *Archives Internationales D'histoire des Sciences*, 29, 104, June–December 1979, pp. 11–12.

4. Andre Wegener Sleeswyk, 'Vitruvius' Odometer' in *Scientific American*, October 1981, pp. 188–200.

5. A. G. Drachmann, *Ktesebios, Philon and Heron*, Munksgaard, Copenhagen, 1948, pp. 6–7.

6. Price, as note 2, p. 53.

7. Joseph Needham, *Science and Civilization in China*, Cambridge University Press, 1965, IV, 2, pp. 82–8.

8. Vitruvius, *De Architectura*, X, iv, 4-v, p. 1.

9. Philo of Byzantium, *Le Livre des Appareils Pneumatiques et des Machines Hydrauliques*, ed. Baron Carra de Vaux, Imprimerie Nationale, Paris, 1903, pp. 118–21, 209–12.

10. Henry Gray, *Anatomy of the Human Body*, ed. Charles M. Gross, Lea & Febiger, Philadelphia, 1959, pp. 145–6.

11. E. W. Marsden, *Greek and Roman Artillery: Technical Treatises*, Clarendon Press, Oxford, 1971, pp. 6–9.

12. (Pseudo-Aristotle), *Mechanical Problems*, section 18.

13. Needham, as note 7, pp. 339–52.

14. E. W. Marsden, *Greek and Roman Artillery: Historical Developments*, Clarendon Press, Oxford, 1969, pp. 201–2.

15. Philo, as note 9, pp. 207–9.

16. Drachmann, as note 5, p. 66.

17. Philo of Byzantium, *Belopoeica*, in note 23, p. 151.

18. Guido Uccelli, *Le Navi de Nemi*, Libreria dello Stato, Rome, 1940, pp. 178–81, and especially figure 192.

19. Lynn White, Jr., *Medieval Technology and Social Change*, Oxford University Press, 1962, pp. 103–91.

20. G. B. Rubin de Cervin, 'Mysteries and Nemesis of the Nemi Ships' in *Mariners Mirror*, XIII, 1955, pp. 38–42.

21. Philo, *Belopoeica*, as note 17, pp. 105–83, especially 146–51.

22. August F. von Pauly and George Wissowa, *Paulys Real-Encyclopädie der classischen Altertumswissenschaft*, J. B. Metzler, Stuttgart, 1894–, 'Dionysius (156)', column 999.

23. Marsden, as note 11, pp. 177–8.

24. *Ibid.*, pp. 179–82.

25. Erwin Schramm, *Die Antiken Geschütze der Saalburg* (ed. by Dietwulf Baatz), Saalburg-Jahrbuch, Saalburgmuseum, Bad Homburg vor der Höhe, 1980, Tafel 7, Abbildung 23.

26. *Ibid.*, pp. 60–2.

27. Drachmann, as note 1, p. 190.

28. Marsden, as note 11, pp. 183–4.

29. Werner Soedel and Vernand Foley, 'Ancient Catapults' in *Scientific American*, March 1979, pp. 150–60.

30. Philo, as note 17, pp. 147, 151.

31. C. J. Longman and Col H. Walrond, *Archery*, Longmans, Green and Co., London, 1894, pp. 425–30.

32. Saxon T. Pope, *Bows and Arrows*, University of California Press, Berkeley, 1962, pp. 31–3.

33. Jacqueline Farmer, 'Secrets of Flight Shooting', in Jack Lewis, *Archer's Digest*, DBI Books, Northfield, Illinois, 1977, pp. 262–7.

34. Philo, as note 17, p. 149.

35. Drachmann, as note 1, p. 202.

36. Needham, as note 7, pp. 339ff, and especially plate CCXXV.

37. Franz Maria Feldhaus, *Die Maschinen im Leben des Volkes*, Verlag Birkhäuser, Basel, 1954, pp. 131, 144.

38. Augustino Ramelli, *Diverse et artificioce machines*, Paris, 1588, Plates 87, 88.

39. Jacques Besson, *Theatre des instruments et machines*, Beroald, Lyon, 1578, figures 36–9, 44.

40. Konrad Kyeser aus Eichstat, *Bellifortis*, ed. Götz Quarg, Verlag der Deutschen Ingenieure, Düsseldorf, 1967, folio 56V. Compare folio 57R.

41. Bertrand Gille, *Engineers of the Renaissance*, MIT Press, Cambridge, Massachusetts, 1966, pp. 15–16, 56.

42. Price, as note 2, pp. 51–4.

43. Sleeswyk, as note 3, pp. 12, 14.

44. Wilbur R. Knorr, 'Archimedes and the *Elements*: Proposal for a Revised Chronological Ordering of the Archimedean Corpus' in *Archive for History of Exact Sciences*, 19, 1, 1978, pp. 211–90.

45. *Ibid.*, pp. 217–23, 268–9.

46. Kurt Mendelssohn, *The Riddle of the Pyramids*, Praeger, New York, 1974, pp. 64, 73–4.

47. Andre Wegener Sleeswyk, 'Reconstruction of the South-Pointing Chariots of The Northern Sung Dynasty. Escapement and Differential Gearing in 11th Century China' in *Chinese Science*, 1977, pp. 4–36.

48. A. E. Berriman, *Historical Metrology*, J. M. Dent, London, 1953, p. 132.

49. Wilbur R. Knorr, 'Archimedes and the Measurement of the Circle: A New Interpretation' in *Archive for History of Exact Sciences*, 15, 1975–6, pp. 115–40.

50. Price, as note 2, pp. 35, 40–5, 60–1.

51. Karl A. Wittfogel, 'The Hydraulic Civilizations,' in William A. Thomas, *Man's Role in Changing the Face of the Earth*, Princeton University Press, Princeton, New Jersey, 1955, pp, 159–60.

The Contributors

MARJORIE N. BOYER is Professor of History at York College of the City of New York. She is the author of *Medieval French Bridges*.

Wm. DAVID COMPTON is a contract historian of technology with a particular interest in space technology. His study of the history of the Skylab project is forthcoming.

FRANCIS EVANS is Lecturer in History of Technology at Sheffield Polytechnic.

VERNARD FOLEY is an associate Professor of History at Purdue University. He has a special interest in the history of technology and in the use of physical and mathematical analysis to supplement literary sources.

MICHAEL FORES, former engineer and civil servant in the Department of Industry, is a freelance writer.

ROMAN MALINOWSKI is Professor of Civil Engineering and Head of the Building Materials Division at Chalmers University of Technology, Goteborg, Sweden.

WERNER SOEDEL is Professor of Mechanical Engineering at Purdue University with special interests in theoretical mechanics and vibrations.

PROFESSOR D.G. TUCKER is Senior Fellow in the History of Technology at the University of Birmingham and a Member of Council of the Newcomen Society.

JOHN TURNER is a 1977 Purdue University graduate in mechanical engineering and is currently employed as a products research engineer.

BRIAN WILHOITE is a 1979 graduate of Purdue University in aeronautical engineering now working on the engineering staff of the space systems group of Rockwell International.

Contents of Former Volumes

Third Annual Volume, 1978

JACK SIMMONS, Technology in History.

R. A. BUCHANAN, History of Technology in the Teaching of History.

P. B. MORICE, The Role of History in a Civil Engineering Course.

JOYCE BROWN, Sir Proby Cautley (1802–71), a Pioneer of Indian Irrigation.

A. RUPERT HALL, On knowing, and knowing how to . . .

FRANK D. PRAGER, Vitruvius and the Elevated Aqueducts.

JAMES A. RUFFNER, Two Problems in Fuel Technology.

JOHN C. SCOTT, The Historical Development of Theories of Wave-Calming using Oil.

Fourth Annual Volume, 1979

P. S. BARDELL, Some Aspects of the History of Journal Bearings and their Lubrication.

K. R. FAIRCLOUGH, The Waltham Pound Lock.

ROBERT FRIEDEL, Parkesine and Celluloid: The Failure and Success of the First Modern Plastic.

J. G. JAMES, Iron Arched Bridge Designs in Pre-Revolutionary France.

L. J. JONES, The Early History of Mechanical Harvesting.

G. HOLLISTER-SHORT, The Sector and Chain: An Historical Enquiry.

Fifth Annual Volume, 1980

THOMAS P. HUGHES, The Order of the Technological World.

THORKILD SCHIØLER, Bronze Roman Piston Pumps.

STILLMAN DRAKE, Measurement in Galileo's Science.

L. J. JONES, John Ridley and the South Australian 'Stripper'.